PLANTS THAT CHANGED
OUR GARDENS

PLANTS THAT CHANGED OUR GARDENS

MEA ALLAN

DAVID & CHARLES

NEWTON ABBOT   LONDON

NORTH POMFRET (VT)   VANCOUVER

ISBN o 7153 6721 8
Library of Congress Catalog Card Number 74–83306
© Mea Allan 1974

Set in 11 on 13 point Baskerville and printed in
Great Britain by Ebenezer Baylis & Son Ltd,
The Trinity Press, Worcester, and London,
for David & Charles (Holdings) Limited,
South Devon House, Newton Abbot, Devon

Published in the United States of America
by David & Charles Inc, North Pomfret
Vermont, 05053, USA

Published in Canada by Douglas David &
Charles Limited, 3645 McKechnie Drive
West Vancouver BC

CONTENTS

5

LIST OF ILLUSTRATIONS

7

Many of the above illustrations, particularly of living plants, are from photographs by Grace Woodbridge

ACKNOWLEDGEMENTS

During the researches for this book I have received valuable
help from many librarians, especially in the search for original
material. Particularly I wish to thank those of the following
libraries: the Arnold Arboretum, Massachusetts; the Botany
Department, the British Museum (Natural History); Cambridge
Botanic Garden and the University Library, Cambridge; the
Royal Botanic Gardens, Kew; the Royal Horticultural Society's
Lindley Library; and for help of this kind on this and previous
books I am grateful to Mrs Elizabeth Acheson and other
members of the staff of the John Innes Institute. I also thank
the families and friends of various of my subjects for the loan
of photographs, letters, diaries and other unpublished material.

M.E.A.

INTRODUCTION

Gardening was late in coming to an art in England. The Romans occupied Britain for over 300 years, in that time making gardens round their houses and villas, as we know from the Saxon names of plants which can be traced to the Latin. But these names are few, so probably the Roman gardens in England were laid out on the same formal lines as those surrounding homeland villas in Italy, relying for their chief attractions on alleys of trees (the Romans introduced the elm), sheltered arbours (we know they grew box), shrubs (of which the cornus was one), and such flowers as the poppy, the mallow and the rose. The barbarous centuries that followed the Roman occupation put an end to what gardens existed, and only with the coming of the monks did they flourish again, though the plants they brought from the continent were chiefly for the *herbularis* or physic garden, with the essential vegetables which formed a large proportion of the daily food in monastery and convent. This is not to say that the monastery garden was devoid of flowers, for even 'herbs' have flowers and we know that roses, violets, poppies, peonies and lilies were grown for medicinal purposes.

But it was not until Elizabeth's reign that gardening as we know it came into its own, when the pattern of living changed from a castle stronghold surrounding a piece of land, to a piece of land surrounding an unprotected dwelling. For Elizabeth's navy had made England strong against invasion, and back with her merchant adventurers came new plants. By 1596 John Gerard, who practised as a barber-surgeon and was Lord Burghley's gardener for over twenty years, was able to list

1,100 different kinds of plants growing in his physic garden at Holborn. They came from many lands, among them '*Ascyron Creticum*, St Peter's woort of Candie', '*Anemone maxima polyanthos*, the great double Windflower of Bithynia', '*Aethiopis*, Aethiopian Mulleine', '*Flos Africanus major*, Great Affrican Marigold', '*Ornithogalum Pannonicum*, Stars of Hungarie', and even '*Campanula elegantissima ex China*, Blew Belflower of China'.

This was the start, and now a world of new floral treasures awaited the new race of plant hunters.

The first of any consequence was John Tradescant who as gardener to the 1st Earl of Salisbury went 'into Flanders and other partes beyonnd the seas' to buy plants for his master's new garden at Hatfield. In 1618, seizing the chance of sailing with a diplomatic mission, he brought back the first plants from Russia. He joined Sir Robert Mansell's expedition against the Barbary corsairs in order to look for new plants in the Mediterranean countries. Again as a gentleman volunteer he joined the Duke of Buckingham on the ill-fated expedition against the Rochellese, and when the new colony of Virginia was being founded he bought shares that entitled him to 100 acres of land. His son John, also a shareholder, three times 'emigrated' there in order to find new plants.

The Hudson's Bay Company was founded in 1670, so by the time David Douglas came on the scene there was a way ready made of securing transport and guides to take him to and fro across the North American continent. The East India Company and the British Governor-General of India furnished facilities for Joseph Hooker. Peter Barr as head of a successful nursery business could go on his own, while E. H. Wilson was sent out by the great nurseryman James Herbert Veitch and then by the Arnold Arboretum. Reginald Farrer was financed by the Royal Horticultural Society and by private garden owners such as Ellen Willmott and E. A. Bowles who wanted their own share of the enormous wealth of plants Farrer was sure he would find in the mountain ranges of the Kansu-Tibetan border.

Thus each plant hunter found his own means of travel, and

each contributed in a different way to make the glory of the English garden as it is today. The Tradescants introduced flowers 'strang and rare' to borders where groundsel and chickweed were still treasured. David Douglas was a man of the trees. Dull Victorian shrubberies were transformed by Joseph Hooker's rhododendrons. Peter Barr made daffodils a first love of our gardens in spring. We owe the Regal Lily and hundreds of beautiful and now familiar shrubs to Ernest Wilson, and to Reginald Farrer floral treasures of the mountains. I have chosen these six to portray the story of plant introductions chronologically, and to show how in the 300 years of that story they changed our gardens stage by stage. For with new shrubs, new trees, new plants of every kind – here was living material out of which to fashion new styles of gardening! Thus with flowers that were a beauty in themselves did the Tradescants oust the geometric knot garden and parterre where flowers were used only to weave a pattern. The herbaceous border came into being, the mixed border where the berries and coloured leaves of shrubs follow the summer flowers. Woodlands were opened so that sunshine could spotlight Wilson's azaleas. Natural rock gardens and scree gardens were created for Reginald Farrer's alpines.

So our debt to the plant hunters is twofold.

It is my hope that this book will tell something of their work and inspire the reader to ask, as he walks round his garden and visits others: 'Who brought this plant to England – and from which country? And when?'

Each has its story, and they are stories of valour, for there is not one plant hunter who left the shores of England to find them but risked his life in the finding.

The question also is twofold: knowing where a plant came from and the kind of home it chose, on rocky steep or by a stream's edge, will help to make you the sort of gardener plants like to grow for, because you understand their needs.

I

THE TRADESCANTS AND THEIR PLANTS 1570–1662

When Thomas Tradescant left his native East Anglia to make his way in the world – which he did, being described as 'yeoman of London' in 1578 when he sold the last of his lands at Henstead in Suffolk – he little thought that his son John would become the first of British plant hunters, bringing to England a wealth of new flowers, shrubs, fruits and trees, become gardener to the King, and finally owner of a famous nursery where strange and rare plants would be eagerly bought by the nobility seeking to vie with each other as owner of the most richly furnished garden.

In the narrow waters English sailors had always held their own, but it was not until Elizabeth's reign that England became mistress of the seas. In 1580 Francis Drake returned to England in the *Golden Hind*, having circumnavigated the world. Three years later Sir Humphrey Gilbert took possession of Newfoundland in the Queen's name. In the following year Philip Amadas and Arthur Barlow touched upon the shores of a new land to be called Virginia and planted as England's first colony. These were voyages of discovery, of evangelism 'calling the pagans into Christianity', of 'noting many things most worthy the observation' such as great fir trees fit to be the masts of ships, bull hides, copper, and pearl called roanoke by the Indian savages. Back came samples of these commodities, among them some first plants, though only a few survived the long journey: it took two months, for instance, to sail back to England from Virginia.

It is not until 1596 that we have any clear idea of what had come into the country, when John Gerard, Lord Burghley's gardener, issued a list of the plants he was cultivating in his garden at Holborn, nearly 1,100 different kinds, both native and foreign. In his famous *Herball*, published in 1597, he tells us where some of them came from. One donor was Master Nicholas Lete, a London merchant who not only searched for plants in England and France but procured them from servants he had in Syria and other countries. It was Lete, for instance, who sent Gerard the 'Gillofloure with yellow flours' which he had procured from Poland. James Cole was another merchant who supplied him with plants, and at one time Gerard employed a collector, William Marshall, whom he 'sent into the Mediterranean' and who returned with seeds of the plane tree and plants of the Prickly Pear. Otherwise William Marshall has not left his mark on the history of plant hunting.

It was the obliging merchants who were Gerard's chief source of what were called exotics or foreign plants. Thus he procured the 'Fig of that part of Spaine called Algarua', the 'Blew Belflower of China' and *'Galeopsis Pannonica'* which he described as the Hungarie Dead Nettle. By 1599 he was growing six different kinds of crocus, ten different irises, sixteen kinds of cherry tree, more than a dozen anemones and several marigolds. Yet still in his garden Bishop's Weed was treasured! And if you know this terrible scourge under this name or that of Ground Elder, you will realise the primitive state of his border plants compared with ours of today. For if he was proud to list *'Chrysanthemum proliferum,* Flower of the Sunne, many on one stalke', he also included weeds like *'Atriplex olida,* Stinking Arach', and *Alsine repens* which was nothing more than chickweed.

In 1629 John Parkinson, apothecary and Herborist to the King, published his *Paradisi in Sole Paradisus Terrestris,* the title of the book a play upon his name, Park-in-Sun's Earthly Paradise. It became the most popular gardening book of the period, and even today gardeners who read its quaint pages cannot fail to be touched by his obvious love of flowers and feeling for their beauty. Parkinson is a recorder of plant-history too, for he sometimes gives actual dates of plant introductions, as when he describes 'The greatest Sea Stocke Gilloflower' (*Matthiola sinuata*) which was 'brought out of the Isle of Ree by Rochel by Mr John Tradescant, when the Duke of Buckingham was sent with supplies for Mounsieur Soubise', and the 'Argier Apricocke' which 'with many other sortes John Tradescante brought with him returning from the Argier voyage, whither hee went voluntary with the Fleete, that went against the Pyrates in the year 1620'.

The name Tradescant recurs again and again in *Paradisus*, and when he came to describe '*Phalangium Virginianum Tradescanti*, Tradescant his Spiderwort' John Parkinson took the opportunity to give a concise biographical account of John Tradescant's career.

'This spider wort is of late knowledge,' he wrote, 'and for it the Christian world is indebted unto that painfull industrious searcher, and lover of all natures varieties, Iohn Tradescant (sometime belonging to the right Honourable Lord Robert Earle of Salisbury ... and then unto ... the Lord Wotton at Canterbury in Kent, and lastly unto the late Duke of Buckingham) ... '

Tradescant was then, in 1629, almost at the height of his career. He must have got his knowledge of the soil and of plants from his yeoman father who probably had a market garden somewhere in London's City or across the river in what was then Surrey. Certainly John was already experienced in horticulture when in 1609 he became head gardener to Sir Robert Cecil, who doubtless knew him well: it is thought that Tradescant was assistant to his father's gardener, John Gerard, at Burghley House in the Strand, and promoted from there. Sir Robert engaged him to lay out the gardens for his new house at Hatfield and to travel in Europe for trees and plants to stock them. From the household accounts of the period, carefully preserved in the Cecil family archives, we have an almost exact knowledge of the plants he bought, how much he paid for them, the routes he travelled and the nurseries in Holland and France where he procured them, as well as the details of how they were collected and transported: by basket and hamper, in river boat and 'wagane', then ship, and finally up the River Lee by wherry to the garden at Hatfield House itself.

He brought back a harvest, enumerated elsewhere,* of trees to make avenues (400 sycamores and hundreds of limes); fruit trees for the orchard (cherries, medlars, apples, pears); soft fruits ('whit curant plants', red currants and black); wall fruits (apricots and peaches). One cherry, which was 'excedyng great', was later called Tradescant's Cherry and is still listed in some catalogues under this name. Reintroduced into Britain early in the present century as the Noble, Edward A. Bunyard, the pomologist, pleaded that the name be stabilised as Tradescant's Heart, to commemorate the man who brought so many new fruits. Others were the Portugal Quince and the Lyons Quince, the white 'Masculine Apricocke', the Archduke's Cherry, the large Dutch Medlar, the Great Red Currant and a black one twice as big as the common English variety.

Among the list of fruit trees was 'Larus Serus', now named *Prunus laurocerasus*, the Cherry Laurel. Eighteen years later it was still a 'rarity' in Parkinson's *Paradisus*. Nurserymen of today give the introduction date of the 'Common or Cherry Laurel' as 1576. But this date refers to its mention in a book of plants published in that year by the Flemish botanist Charles l'Ecluse, whose name is better known Latinised as Clusius. He lived in Antwerp, and the laurel he grew, sent to him from Trebizond, was the common one. John Tradescant the younger in his catalogue of garden plants published in 1656 separates the Common from the Cherry Laurel, and he was then growing

* Mea Allan, *The Tradescants: Their Plants, Gardens and Museum 1570–1662* (1964).

four others: the Spurge Laurel, the 'true Laurell of Alexandria' (*Danae racemosa*, which his father had introduced before 1634), 'Laurus Gallica' (*L. nobilis*) which he knew as 'French Bayes', and the Portugal Laurel, subjected to heavy clipping in Victorian days but beautiful if allowed to develop naturally.

It was a 'viag of ambusad' that give the first John Tradescant his opportunity to visit Russia, a new field for botanists. This was in 1618. The 1st Lord Salisbury had died in 1611, tragically without ever inhabiting Hatfield House. William, his eldest son, was more lavish in refurbishing the various residences he inherited than in paying his gardener's salary. But before John left Hatfield he went abroad to procure roses of all kinds for the Salisbury garden in the Strand, and for hedging. As John Evelyn tells us in his *Sylva*: 'John Tradescant brought a small *Ozier* from St Omer in Flanders, which makes incomparable Networks ... ' This was *Salix elaeagnus*, the Hoary Willow. Then, some time between the autumn of 1614 and June 1615, we find Tradescant at work in the gardens of St Augustine's Palace, close by Canterbury Cathedral, as gardener to Sir Edward Wotton. Nearby was Chilham where Wotton's friend Sir Dudley Digges was building a grand new house. It was arranged that John Tradescant should lay out the garden for him. The two became friendly, and in 1618 when King James despatched Sir Dudley to Russia to give financial help to the young Tsar, in the hope of securing exclusive trade privileges in return, John Tradescant went with him.

The plants he brought back added a new rose to our gardens, 'Rosa Moscovitica', with a plant 'bearing his fruit like hedgemercury', a 'sorrell half the heyght of a man', a 'bery muche lik a strabery but of an amber coller', and 'two sorts of blewe whorts'. Translated into modern names, the Russian rose is unidentifiable, though we know it was single and that its scent was 'marvelus sweete', as Tradescant's companions informed him: he himself, sadly for a plant hunter, lacked any 'sence of smelling'. He found it in the Dvina delta, with others covering four or five acres of the appropriately named Rose Island, and it was still growing in the Tradescants' old garden at Lambeth in 1814. The plant with fruit like hedge-mercury was *Cornus suecica*, the creeping dogwood with white bracts. The amber berry was *Rubus chamaemorus*, called by the Russians *moroschka*. 'Sorrell half the heyght of a man' was *Oxydendrum arboreum* which grows 20ft tall in Britain, and whose leaves turn beautiful shades of red in the autumn. Of the 'blewe whorts', one was *Vaccinium myrtillus*, the bilberry or whortleberry.

But his greatest find was the larch tree. He called it a fir and entered it in his garden list as 'Abies', the name it was given before it was subdivided as *Larix*. He brought home cones and succeeded in raising trees from their seed, planting some at Newhall, near Chelmsford, when he became gardener to George Villiers, Duke of Buckingham, in 1625. They were of good stature by the time John Evelyn saw them in 1656. The larch has since become one of our most valuable timber trees, and with its feathery foliage it is a decoration for any garden, in spring decked with little crimson flowers, in autumn a blaze of russet.

In order to travel abroad in those days, one had to seek ways and means. December 1620 saw John Tradescant climbing aboard the pinnace *Mercury* as a gentleman volunteer against the corsairs of Barbary who were harassing British merchant shipping in the Mediterranean. Captain of the vessel was Phineas Pett, Commissioner of the Navy, who was heavily in debt and anxious to keep out of England as long as possible. He succeeded in staying abroad for seven months, as he records in his autobiography. The campaign was fruitless, and long after Mansell and his fleet had returned to Plymouth, *Mercury* was still sailing about the Mediterranean.

It was from this voyage that the lilac came to our gardens. Tradescant called it 'Jasminum Persicum, the violet-coloured

Persian Jasmine'. What would our gardens be without lilacs?

Another important find was the Horse Chestnut, said to have been brought to England from Tibet in 1550, yet still described by Gerard in 1579 as a rare foreign tree 'which groweth in Italy and in sundry places of the East-countries'. In Johnson's edition of the *Herball*, it was 'now growing with Mr Tradescant at South Lambeth'; and Parkinson, in 1629, says, 'Our Christian world had first a knowledge of it from Constantinople.'

Another new plant was *Gladiolus byzantinus*, the Corn Flag. 'With this species John Tradescant observed many acres of ground overspread', Parkinson tells us. The carpet of carmine flower-spikes must have been an amazing sight.

It was spring in the Mediterranean when John Tradescant found his Great Rose Daffodil, which must have caused a sensation when he grew it at Lambeth. In his *Paradisus* Parkinson featured 'this Prince of Daffodils', as he called it, in a drawing showing the petal-upon-petal rose formation. E. A. Bowles in his *Handbook of Narcissus* mistakenly described it as having a double trumpet. The Rose Daffodil has no trumpet and opens into a great six-pointed star. Alas, nurserymen do not cultivate it nowadays, though it still exists in old gardens having a past connection with the Tradescant family.

There were other daffodils, crocuses, anemones. In his 1634 *Plantarum in Horto* John Tradescant lists more than twenty-four different daffodils he was growing (not counting such lumpings as 'diversae species' and 'aliae diversae species'), against only a dozen in Gerard's 1599 list. Many of them were therefore new.

Those who garden on a chalk or alkaline soil may deplore the fact that they cannot grow rhododendrons. We can, however, grow the cistus, the Sun Rose which every day opens a fresh mantle of flowers. In 1656 John Tradescant the younger was growing eleven different kinds, at least six being his father's introductions, three of which he had brought back from his Mediterranean trip with Phineas Pett. These were *C. monspeliensis*, the Montpelier Rock Rose with sticky leaves and pure white flowers; *C. hirsutus*, a dwarf species with conspicuous yellow stamens in white flowers; and *C. ladanifer*, the Gum Cistus, also white but with a chocolate basal stain. *C. populifolius* was sent to him from Spain in 1632, and *C. crispus* from Portugal. Later he introduced *C. corbariensis*, one of the hardiest, *C. laxus*, and *C. albidus* of white downy leaves and pale rosy-lilac flowers. A cousin of these enchanting shrubs which Tradescant also found in 1620 was *Halimium halimifolium*, which he called the 'Sea-Purslan leafed Cistus'. This is a small erect shrub with narrow grey leaves, producing a flush of bright yellow flowers from May onwards.

A celandine rare in gardens, with big waxy yellow flowers, was another Mediterranean treasure (*Ranunculus ficaria* var. *grandiflorus*), with what Tradescant called 'Hypertricum latifolium Lusitanicum', which can be none other than *H. calycinum*, the now-familiar Rose of Sharon, invaluable as ground-cover in dry and shady places; the white lupin, which he brought from Crete, a lovely iris he called the Persian Flower-de-luce (*Iris persica*); and *Cytisus canariensis*, the 'Genista' of the florists. There were many more. Gerard had a single '*Lychnis Chalcedonica*', or Nonesuch of Constantinople: Tradescant introduced one with double flowers. He brought the rush-leaved coronilla, and the lovely Willow Gentian, besides a most useful item for the kitchen garden – *Lactuca scariola*, the Cos Lettuce, from the island of that name. This was the second lettuce he had introduced, the other being the red-leaved Roman Cos which he first brought into England for the Hatfield garden. A most interesting find was *Acanthus spinosus*, the Prickly Bear's Breeches (though how it got its name I cannot tell). He found it in Italy and we know it as a dramatic herbaceous plant with tall spikes of pink and maroon, and green berries in the autumn.

Let us finish the Mediterranean harvest with three more treasures: two jasmines and a tree. If you grow *Jasminum humile*, as I do, you will know that it is indeed a treasure, for although its showers of yellow blossoms are scentless (John's seventeenth-century word for it was 'unsavoury'), its leaves keep green all the year. As for the other, this was the tender *Jasminum grandiflorum* of fragrant white flowers, which he found in Portugal. The tree was *Pistacia terebinthus*, not the source of pistachio nuts but the Chian Turpentine Tree, still grown for its dark glossy aromatic leaves as a small tree or large shrub.

Like Gerard, John Tradescant had his obliging collectors, one of whom was Sir Henry Wotton, brother of his employer and ambassador at Venice. About December 1622 he received from him 'Finocchio' or Italian fennel, with directions for bleaching its stems to make them tender.

John Tradescant had married at Meopham in Kent in 1607, and in the following year their son was born. John junior was a clever boy. He was admitted a King's Scholar at the King's School, Canterbury, when he was eleven. In the same year that he left school, 1623, his father became gardener to George Villiers, Duke of Buckingham, who was the brilliant star at the court of King James I. No doubt young John became assistant to his father when he laid out the Duke's gardens at Newhall and planted the mile-long avenue of lime trees in four rows admired by John Evelyn in 1656. Buckingham had sent his gardener to the Low Countries to buy them.

Life as Buckingham's gardener took on many interesting aspects. In 1625, shortly after Charles I succeeded to the throne, Tradescant accompanied his master to Paris to bring home the little Henrietta Maria, sister of Louis XIII. It was an odd arrangement; for although she was to be England's new Queen, Buckingham was first to marry her by proxy. To John the trip to Paris meant a visit to Jean Robin and his son Vespasien. Robin was the first Herborist to the French King, and his son was to become one of France's greatest plant hunters, following his father as later did John Tradescant the younger. When the gardeners Jean and John got together, you can imagine what happened – the exchanging of plants and the cementing of a great gardening friendship. John had already sent seeds and berries to Robin from his Russian trip, and in the blank pages of his copy of Parkinson's *Paradisus*, where he recorded plants received after its publication and until 1633, we read of plants sent 'from Mr Robine' and 'from Mounser Robyne' – roses, irises, anemones, 'on Red Honnysoccle' which later he called 'the German red indented Honisockle'. This may have been *Lonicera periclymenum* var. *serotina*. If so, it was a new addition to our garden flowers. Also from Robin came the glorious bronze-leaved Cardinal Flower from America, and a cutting of 'Arbutus, sive Unedo'. This was the Strawberry Tree, now one of the most ornamental of all our garden trees, with its red bark, panicles of white pitcher-shaped flowers, glossy evergreen leaves and strawberry fruits. When Dr William Watson visited the old Lambeth garden in 1749 there were two trees of the Arbutus still there, the largest he had ever seen. In 1629 Robin sent a 'Tragacantha slipe', which was of *Astragalus tragacantha*, the Goat's-thorn, a rock-garden shrub of pea-shaped flowers in May and June.

It was through Robin that another ornament came to our gardens, when the French herborist sent his English friend the tree which now bears his name, *Robinia pseudacacia*. Think of it on a hot summer's day with its black bark, the greenest of feathery leaves and long racemes of white scented flowers. Robin first had this tree in 1621 – or was it John Tradescant who gave it to Robin? In his *Theatrum Botanicum*, published in 1640, Parkinson tells us that 'A very like tree' was of 'an exceeding height with Master Tradescant'. So it must have been older than nineteen years. John called it 'Locusta Virginiana arbor', and it is in fact the same tree.

When he accompanied the Duke of Buckingham to the island of Rhé on the ill-fated expedition against the Rochellese, John returned not only with *Matthiola sinuata*, from which our Ten Weeks Stocks have been developed, but with a lovely plant of silver leaves – the Sea Wormwood which with its cousins of the Artemisia tribe are popular nowadays with flower arrangers. Another plant from Rhé was the Corn Rose or Corn Poppy, from which the Shirley Poppy has descended. For it must be remembered that some of these early introductions bore quite modest flowers when they were first cultivated in our gardens. We owe a debt of gratitude to those who, by cross-fertilisation and the careful selection of seedlings, sometimes over a span of many years, evolved flowers of greater size, increased beauty and more varied colours. It was the Rev William Wilks, secretary of the Royal Horticultural Society, who one day, walking in his garden at Shirley, looked over his fence and saw a white poppy growing among the red ones. He saved its seed, sowed it in his garden, saved the seeds of those flowers, and went on until he had stabilised the Shirley Poppy as a new race. In this same way were the flowers John Tradescant's son brought from Virginia to become some of our garden favourites.

Meanwhile, in 1626, the Tradescants took up residence in South Lambeth. Their house and garden soon became famous throughout the Western world, the house as a 'Closett of Rarities', full of the curiosities John had picked up in his travels, which one day were to go to Oxford as the Ashmolean Museum; the acres round the house a mecca for garden-lovers and botanists. Peter Munday, the traveller, visited the Ark (as it was called) before he went to the Far East. John Ray came to study new plants, and Thomas Johnson to describe them for his new edition of Gerard's *Herball*. A plant that greatly took his fancy was the graceful Queen of the Meadows, which some said was but a wild plant. Johnson was a much-travelled man, going out on botanical forays all over the English countryside, and he declared: 'I have not yet heard of it wild with us, but only seene it growing with Mr Tradescant.' Owners of gardens large and small came to buy trees and shrubs, border plants and bulbs. And so the floral riches John Tradescant had introduced from many parts of the world spread around Britain.

He was still the Duke of Buckingham's gardener. Young John, eighteen now, was well able to look after the Lambeth garden and nursery when his father was away from home. Then in 1628, as he was preparing for another assault on Rochelle,

Buckingham was assassinated. He must often have spoken to the King about his gardener, extolling his worth, for it was not long afterwards that John Tradescant took up his new appointment as Keeper of His Majesty's Garden, at the princely salary of £100 a year.

There was no more plant hunting for him. But he had an active agent in Sir Edward Nicholas, Buckingham's one-time secretary who was now Secretary to the Admiralty. Through him sea captains and ambassadors abroad were alerted, and soon ships returning to England were carrying the 'slipes, seedes and rootes' John had asked for. Among them at this time may have been his introduction of that favourite of the florists, the Scabious (*Scabiosa atropurpurea*) or Pincushion Flower; the attractive shrub called Jupiter's Beard (*Anthyllis barba-jovis*) with silvery leaves and clusters of cream-coloured flowers; and another shrub, also with silvery leaves, *Atriplex halimus*, which is very good for seaside gardens.

Some of the new plants coming to South Lambeth were from Virginia, in which John the elder had a proprietary interest, for in 1616 when he was at Canterbury he became a shareholder of the Virginia Company, having heard stories of the wonderful plants to be found in the colony. The share entitled him to fifty acres of land: John took it out in plants, Captain Samuel Argall (who regularly plied across the Atlantic with emigrants) promising to send him back anything he thought interesting. The first was Moses in the Bulrushes, the whole genus being named by Linnaeus *Tradescantia* in John's honour. Another was that autumn glory, the Virginia Creeper, which John called the Virginian Ivy or Vine, though we must now call it by its new name *Partdenocissus quinquefolia*.

From then onward Virginian plants came to him from time to time. It was not until John the younger went to the colony in person that the few became many, and the many a rich contribution in plants that changed our gardens with glorious colours and shapes hitherto unknown.

His first recorded visit was in 1637. A State Paper, Colonial,

26

tells us that in this year he was 'in the colony, to gather all rarities of flowers, plants, shells, etc.'. He stayed until the following year, as we know from Parkinson's sad comment on the 'Berry bearing Ferne of America, which Mr John Tradescant the younger brought home with him from Virginia this present year, 1638, presently after the death of his father'. This was *Adiantum pedatum*, the Shield Fern.

He returned to the New World in 1642 and again in 1654, his name being listed as a passenger taking up headrights granted in these years. But unless the Tradescants had a zealous agent working for them in Virginia, it is probable that John the younger visited the colony in 1632. Between 1629 and 1633 his father recorded American introductions that were 'Received': one in 1629, one in 1630, eleven in 1632, nine in 1633. Then in 1634 when his *Plantarum in Horto* was printed, there is a flood of twenty-nine American plants, all additional to those 'Received' from 1630 to 1633. This indicates that John the younger himself brought them back.

Travellers to Virginia never forgot their first impression of it, vividly recorded in the despatch Philip Amadas and Arthur Barlow wrote to Sir Walter Raleigh in 1584. 'The second of July, we found shole water, wher we smelt so sweet, and so strong a smel, as if we had bene in the midst of some delicate garden abounding with all kinde of odiferous flowers ... '

They viewed the land about them. It was sandy and low, 'but so full of grapes, as the very beating and surge of the Sea overflowed them'. They grew on the hills, in the plains, on every little shrub, and climbed to the tops of even high cedars, which were the 'highest and reddest cedars of the world'. John the younger brought back two different grapes: *Vitis labrusca*, the Fox Grape; and *V. riparia* (*V. vulpina*), the Riverbank Grape. The first became the parent of most of the cultivated American grapes. The other is a useful climber worth growing for its mignonette-scented flowers and bright green foliage, to say nothing of its purple-black fruits. Incidentally, it is interesting that John the younger translated *Vitis vulpina* (literally 'fox') as the Fox Grape. Systematists have done a switch, but have substituted the epithet *riparia* which at least tells us that this grape grew on the bank of a river.

Meanwhile let us see what Virginian treasures his father had introduced. *Rhus typhina* came to him in 1629, in which year John Parkinson recorded it. This was the brilliant-leaved Sumach, a colourful addition to our gardens, which Tradescant received from Mr Humphrey Slany of the Newfoundland Company of London and a shareholder in Virginia.

Then came the Allegheny Foamflower (*Tiarella cordifolia*) with its spikes of white starry flowers; the Virginian Snakeweed (*Aristolochia serpentaria*); the Golden Rod (*Solidago canadensis*), forerunner of autumn in our herbaceous borders, with another favourite, the Cone Flower (*Rudbeckia laciniata*), sent to him by Vespasien Robin. There was also the 'Milk-white Daffodil', which was *Hymenocallis caribaea*, and the white-flowered Hemp Agrimony (*Eupatorium ageratoides*). Nobody had ever before seen *Ptelea trifoliata*. This was the Hop Tree whose small yellowish flowers are as fragrant as any honeysuckle.

Autumn in our gardens would be nothing without the Michaelmas Daisy of glorious blues, wines and purples. Its first parent came to the South Lambeth garden in 1633, and Thomas Johnson noted it growing there, not so splendid a plant as nowadays decks our borders but splendid enough to cause comment. It was not until after 1891 that the Michaelmas Daisy was hybridised and brought to perfection. Linnaeus named the original *Aster Tradescanti* in honour of the man who introduced it. A useful tree came in the same year, *Juglans cinerea*, the Canadian walnut or Butternut. Fast-growing and attractive with its large hairy leaves, this is good for the smaller garden, as it grows only to medium size and has exceptionally large fruits. Listed in every good fruit catalogue is *Juglans nigra*, the black walnut which the elder Tradescant introduced and was growing in his garden in 1634.

The early settlers in Virginia sought plants known to be of medicinal value. One was Asarum, used by the Indians to cure the terrible colics from which they suffered, and this was another 1633 introduction: John Tradescant knew it as 'Asarum majus Americanum, American Asirabacca', the now-named *Asarum virginianum*.

The Butterfly Weed (*Asclepias purpurascens*) makes a handsome border plant with its umbels of crimson-purple lobed flowers and pale red or purple hoods. Thank John Tradescant for it.

Some of our most colourful shrubs and trees have come from Virginia. Picture the autumn woods aflame with the Liquid-ambar! This, the Sweet Gum, was yet another introduction by John the elder, sometimes confused with the maples but easily identified by its alternate leaves. There was the Persimmon (*Diospyros virginiana*) whose yellow and red fruits among brilliant leaves brought us another glory of the Virginian autumn. The Shagbark Hickory was valued by the Indians for its nuts: today *Carya ovata* is still the most valuable nut-producing species in the USA and is treasured in Britain for its rich yellow autumn foliage.

Captain John Smith, who was saved from death by the Indian Princess Pocohontas, was an early adventurer to whom we are also indebted for descriptions of Virginia when it was 'as God first made it'; and George Percy in his *True Discourse* tells of the primeval forest rioting with climbing plants, the strawberries so thick that the wanderer's feet were dyed with their blood. Perhaps it was Captain Smith who brought back the strawberry to John Tradescant who was his close friend: he bequeathed to him some of his books, and they are now in the Bodleian Library. The strawberry was *Fragaria virginiana*, 'mother' of our Keen's Seedlings and Scarlet and British Queen varieties. And while we are in the kitchen garden, let us mention *Phaseolus coccineus*, the Scarlet Runner Bean. These were toothsome acquisitions.

Of the climbers, the Passion Flower ran riot everywhere, its fruits called Amaracocks by the Indians. Gerard does not mention it in his 1599 garden list, but it is described in Parkinson's *Paradisus*, and certainly the elder Tradescant was growing it in 1634. He called it 'Flos Passionis, vel Maracoc: Passion-flower'. Its Latin name is now *Passiflora incarnata*. What a fascinating climber it makes on a sunny house wall, in good summers producing its delicious fruits. You may wonder how it got its name? The curious flowers bear a fancied resemblance to the instruments of Christ's Passion: the leaf symbolising the spear; the five anthers the five wounds; the tendrils the cords or whips; the column of the ovary the pillar of the cross; the stamens the hammers; the three styles the three nails; the fleshy threads within the flowers the crown of thorns; the calyx the glory or nimbus; the white tint purity; the blue tint heaven. The Passion Flower keeps open for three days, symbolising the three years' ministry. Children love looking for its marks. Indeed, the Passion Flower makes a good first lesson in botany.

John Tradescant also grew *Clematis virginiana*, which he called Virginian Lady's Bower. The Royal Horticultural Society's *Dictionary of Gardening* gives its introduction date as 1767, but it was already flourishing in the Lambeth garden in 1634.

It is difficult to identify some of the early introductions by their old Latin names. What, for instance, would you make of 'Convolvulus Virginianus, cordato folio, flore obsoleto, Tradescanti'? Let us analyse it: Tradescant's convolvulus with cordate (heart-shaped) leaves and rudimentary flowers. Could this be what we know as *Cocculus carolinus*, an earlier introduction than the RHS dictionary's 1759? Though its flowers are insignificant, it is useful for covering trellis-work in sun or semi-shade, and, if you wish, will climb into hedges and trees. Tradescant, who put his name to it, was certainly very proud of it.

What better to put on our scratches after pruning roses than cooling Wych Hazel? It comes from the bark and leaves of *Hamamelis virginiana* whose clusters of fragrant brownish-yellow flowers come in September and October, when the foliage itself turns bright yellow. I am at odds again with the RHS dictionary which says it came from eastern North America in 1736, for Parkinson refers to it under its old synonym 'Pistachia nigra corylifolius'. The Parkinson date may indicate a 'hidden' tribute to John Tradescant.

It is easier when we come to *Lupinus perennis*, which John listed in 1634. This was one of the parents of our border lupins, and there is no doubt about *Dodecatheon meadia*, the American Cowslip or Shooting Star, which he called 'Tradescant his greatest blush Beares ears'; umbels of charming rose-coloured flowers with their petals turned back.

The Evening Primrose (*Oenothera biennis*) is a Tradescant flower I would not be without, for its scent when the sun goes down and the glimmering light from its lemon petals. John gave us the yellow Virginian pansy (*Viola pubescens*) and the Virginian rose which Graham S. Thomas, the leading authority on old shrub roses, thinks was probably the parent of the exquisite Rose d'Amour or St Mark's Rose.

Two smilacinas also came from Virginia: *S. racemosa*, a woodland plant like Solomon's Seal; and *S. stellata* which we call the Star-flowered Lily of the Valley.

Let us have a look at the Lambeth garden where all these plants were growing. Its site is marked by two roads: Tradescant Road, which speaks for itself, and Walberswick Street for the Suffolk village where lived Tradescant cousins Thomas and Robert to whom John the younger left legacies. The Tradescants' Lambeth home was called Turret House and it stood until 1880 when the extent of its garden was 4 acres, 14 perches. It was larger when the Tradescants lived there, as Dr André Coltée Ducarel wrote to William Watson in 1772. Ducarel was then living in the front part of the house and knew that the garden had extended a good way to the north 'and took in not only my orchard and garden but also two or three of my next neighbours' '. He described Turret House as a 'great house', and an old print certainly shows it as an imposing building. Inside, it was a place of gracious living. Framed in the oak panelling of the dining-room were portraits of the family, found

31

on the day Turret House was sold for demolition and now in the Ashmolean Museum at Oxford.

As to the garden, we know what it looked like in 1691, only thirteen years after the death of Hester, John the younger's second wife. A Captain Foster then lived in the house, and in the garden was 'the finest striped hollyhedge that is perhaps in England'. There were many myrtles cut in fanciful shapes, and a framed walk of timber covered with vines which with others running on most of the walls yielded Captain Foster 'a deal of wine'. The Tradescants grew thirteen different kinds of grapes. And, of course, we know from the *Musaeum Tradescantianum*, which catalogues not only the rarities and curiosities collected on their travels by both Johns, and those donated by bene-factors, but everything growing in their garden – which must have been a wonderful place, containing the greatest gathering together in Britain of all kinds of plants, from 'the little single violet coloured Periwincle' and 'the little Mallow-leafed Bird-weed' to shrubs and noble trees. There was a collection of mosses, and of rock plants such as arabis, stonecrop, saxifrages, dwarf irises, soldanellas, Creeping Jenny, sedums and Rock Roses – and who would not wish to grow, as the Tradescants did, 'Myagrum monospermon, the one grain'd gold of pleasure'?

There was a pond in which they grew aquatic plants: what they called 'Sambucas aquatica, water-Elder' (now translated as the Guelder Rose, which the Tradescants also grew, so it must have been something different), the Small Water Valerian and Great Water Valerian, with 'Stellata aquatica, the water-Starwort'. Round the pond would be growing *Osmunda regalis* which John the younger also called 'Filix florida, water-Ferne, or Sun-Royall', the double Marsh Marigolds and, surely, mirrored in the water, his Swamp Cypress. As for the kitchen garden and orchard, we already know that John the elder was famed for his fruit trees and vegetables. You would probably find not much difference from your own kitchen garden if you could walk back in time beyond that striped holly hedge and see the neat rows of turnips, parsnips and spinach, lettuces,

Page 33 (right)
John Tradescant, gardener to King Charles I and first of the great plant hunters. From his famous Lambeth nursery he distributed flowers 'strang and rare'

(left) John Tradescant the younger who succeeded his father as royal gardener. The plants he introduced from Virginia brought a wealth of new colour to English gardens

Page 34 (left) Tradescantia virginiana, called Moses in the Bulrushes from the blue 'eyes' of its flowers. It came to England from the new colony in 1614.

(right) the glorious Ten Weeks Stocks whose ancestor was John the elder's 'greatest Sea Stocke Gilloflower'

parsley, beans (six different kinds), and even three different kinds of tomato (which they called by their old name, Apples of Love), with rhubarb, pot herbs, and potatoes – which would not be the smooth oval shape they are today: they did not emerge from their knobbly state until some time later, again by careful selection of young stock.

What a garden it was! There were hollyhocks and pansies, tree mallows, eleven different lilies, Canterbury Bells and corn-flowers, salvias, catmint for the household cat (the Tradescants called the plant 'Mentha Cattaria'), seven kinds of poppy, five pulmonarias, thirty-two roses, nine primroses including those old charmers like Jackanapes-on-Horseback, Gaskins and Hose-in-Hose, so sought-after today. Among the spring-flowering bulbs were 'a great variety of gallant Tulips' (more than thirty different ones), twenty-nine sorts of daffodil, and the little cyclamens that love to grow under trees, with a dozen colchi-cums, both spring- and autumn-flowering.

Of these there were scores of John the elder's introductions, and if we are looking at the 1656 list there were as many new ones his son introduced.

We can definitely identify a plant as theirs where John or his son clearly labelled it as being 'of Tradescant', viz 'Phalangium Virginianum Tradescanti', the white-flowered Tradescantia which John the younger brought from the New World; and sometimes Parkinson specifically states that one or the other introduced this or that species. At other times, introductions which may be theirs are described without a credit. Had we a Tradescant garden-list pre-1629 and could compare it with Gerard's 1599 list, we would probably find many more plants that were Tradescant introductions. However, knowing where the two travelled and when, by honest comparison with Gerard's and other lists, even going back to that of Coys, and using Linnaeus's *Species Plantarum* as a translator, we can with-out jumping to conclusions and without doubt identify a considerable number of them.

In 1637 when John the younger went to the New World to

see for himself the land whence had come so many colourful plants, he hoped to find ones as yet undiscovered. He left behind him his nine-year-old daughter Frances and three-year-old son John. Jane, his wife, had died two years before.

Sixteenth-century travellers to Virginia, as for instance Sir Walter Raleigh's cousin Sir Richard Grenville in 1585, took a circuitous route via the Canary Islands, hugging the coasts as long as they could before breasting the open Atlantic. A month later, borne on the north equatorial current, they arrived at Dominica in the West Indies where they were glad to land again, to take in fresh provisions. There were delays: ten days were spent in building a new pinnace, and they were 'stung ... with the Muskitos'. But there were gains too. Grenville captured two Spanish frigates which they afterwards ransomed for 'good round summes'. Twenty-five days later they sighted Florida and crept up the coast. Virginia itself was puzzling. There were islands thought to be the mainland, and great stretches of water thought to be a sea. John's ship would probably take a more direct route after the West Indies, reaching the Virginian islands perhaps in thirty-seven days, as did Philip Amadas and Arthur Barlow.

In Barbados John collected what he called 'Herba Sensitiva humilis', that extraordinary plant *Mimosa pudica*, which today is being used to detect radio-activity. A dried specimen of it had been seen in November 1632 at Trinity House by Thomas Johnson, and since then stories had been circulating about it, how it would shrink at the touch of a finger or indeed from any object presented to it. Now here was the real thing!

Another weird plant which fell to John's trowel was *Sarracenia purpurea*, variously called the Huntsman's Horn, the Side-Saddle Flower and, more commonly, the Pitcher Plant. The strange formation of the leaves, which were hollow and shaped exactly like a hunting horn, even having a lid to close it, excited John Parkinson who wrote of it in his *Theatrum*: 'Of late Master John Tradescant the Younger found this very plant in Virginia, having his toppe thereon, which he brought home and groweth with him.' John called it the Seamarch Buglass, which indicates that he found it on the salt-flats near the shore.

There were great rivers and vast swamps. John, we know, was in Virginia in the autumn of 1637, for Parkinson tells us that he did not return to England until after the death of his father. Tradescant the elder died in April 1638. So it was some time in October that young John saw his first Swamp Cypress, standing like a burning torch in the Virginian sunshine. He picked a pocketful of the globular cones. Parkinson records: 'Its seed was brought by Master Tradescant from Virginia, and sown here and doe spring very bravely.' Since then, *Taxodium distichum* has sprung bravely in many commercial nurseries, and found good homes all over Britain. But it likes its feet wet! If you have a lake or pond, plant it by the water's edge, and when its foliage turns bronze in the autumn, remember Master Tradescant.

Another tree that was to do great things was *Platanus occidentalis*. This was the Buttonwood whose seed balls hang from its branches like strings of beads. John could never have guessed that in a few years it was to father the London Plane by its marriage with *Platanus orientalis*. But this is what happened. The European plane was already growing in the Lambeth garden, and when John's Buttonwood seedlings were ready for their permanent quarters he planted one nearby. John the elder had been appointed the first Keeper of the Oxford Botanic Garden in 1637, but by then he was too ill to accept the post and Jacob Bobart was appointed in his place, though not until about 1642. The Botanic Garden, being new, had to be stocked, and it would be strange if young John did not send some trees and other plants to commemorate his father. The original *Platanus acerifolia* (*occidentalis* x *orientalis*) was first discovered in the Oxford Botanic Garden. The London Plane is now one of our most useful as well as most beautiful of trees, tolerating the smoky atmospheres of cities yet keeping itself clean by discarding its old bark. John thought his tree was an Acer, and called it 'his other Virginian Maple', referring to 'Acer

Virginianum Tradescanti, Tradescant's Virginian Maple', which we shall come to later.

Becoming more and more popular in our gardens are the Polygonums, some low-growing with heather-looking pink spikes, others bushy with white or crimson panicles. John brought home *Polygonum virginianum*, which is a perennial 2–5ft tall and with greenish flowers in slender racemes sometimes 10in long. It is a hardy plant blooming from August to October.

He also brought three climbers. One was *Gelsemium sempervirens*, and Parkinson had a friendly comment on this False Jasmine with the sweet-smelling yellow flowers. 'It groweth in Virginia as Master Tradescant who saw it there doth affirme, and from him I have a plant, risen of the seede.' Another, which John also called a jasmine, was *Campsis radicans*, the Trumpet Vine. This is a beautiful thing, with brilliant orange and scarlet flowers which are trumpet-shaped and 2–3in long. Normally it climbs by aerial roots, so, if you grow it, give it a little support until it is established. It flowers in August and September. The third climber John found was the Trumpet Honeysuckle (*Lonicera sempervirens*), with flowers rich orange-scarlet outside and yellow within. But this was already in the Lambeth garden, for it had been sent to his father some time before 1634, if John did not bring it himself. Doubtless, though, he took some of its seeds home, for it was a striking species and very popular.

We have one last plant credited to John for this trip: *Aquilegia canadensis*, which is the first recorded aquilegia apart from the common wild columbine. It became a parent of our long-spurred garden strains, and in itself is surely one of our best-loved border plants. Its flowers are bright canary yellow tinged with red.

John came home to a house of mourning. His famous father had been buried with ceremony, the Great Bell of St Mary's,

Lambeth, tolling for him. He had died a man of some property, leaving to his son his lease in South Lambeth and his lease in Woodham Water, the latter acquired when he was gardening for the Duke of Buckingham at Newhall.

The seal on his will is that of the Tradescant arms: three fleur-de-lys on a bend or, surmounted by a vase holding a fleur-de-lys with two leaves. These flowers stood for his connection with the French Henrietta Maria, for although appointed by King Charles as the royal gardener, John the elder seems to have been paid by the Queen. Now in the midsummer of 1638 John the younger was appointed in his father's place. The salary was the same, £100 a year. In October he married Hester Pooks.

In 1642 headrights were granted for 650 acres on the north side of the Charles River (now York River) in Peanpetanke Creek, and east upon a great creek near the oyster shell bank. They were to be divided among thirteen persons. John Tradescant was one of them. He brought back some wonderful things from this visit and from that of 1654 when again he was granted headrights, this time at Payankatank, somewhere within the area of modern Yorktown, York County, and Belfield. They are marked on an old colonial map of Virginia as Plots 25 and 28. On these visits he had a friend in Virginia waiting to show him new plants and trees. This was Edward Digges, fourth son of his father's friend Sir Dudley.

It is difficult to know on which of the two visits John collected each particular plant among those new Virginian ones listed in his catalogue of 1656, for in most cases we now have only this date to go on. But it does not really matter. What is important is that by 1656 the Lambeth garden was the richer by many more Virginian treasures, and because John was by now as famous a nurseryman as his father other gardens were benefiting from his plant hunting. So let us treat them together.

He was a man who loved trees, as is evident from the number he collected. One of his greatest finds was *Acer rubrum*. This was 'the' Virginian maple, as against his 'other' one, and

John proudly called it 'Acer Virginianum Tradescanti, *Tradescant's Virginian Maple*'. We know this glorious tree as the Red or Canadian Maple, whose dark green palmate leaves turn rich red and scarlet in the autumn, especially when it grows in an acid soil.

The Pawpaw Tree was greatly valued by the American Indians for its fruit. In its native land it grew to be a tree of up to 40ft tall, and thinking to add to our orchards John brought home some of its seeds to propagate. In Britain, however, it rarely grows beyond shrub size and hardly ever develops fruit. But if *Asimina triloba* was a disappointment he had better luck with another tree valued by the Indians for alleviating toothache. This was *Zanthoxylum americanum*, the Toothache Tree or Prickly Ash, whose small yellowish-green flowers in spring are followed by clusters of jet-black fruits. Another success was *Celtis occidentalis*, the North American Hackberry, Lote or Nettle Tree, which we know from John Ray was the younger Tradescant's introduction. It also produced black fruits in profusion. It is to John Aubrey that we owe the information that John the younger introduced *Cedronella triphylla*. When he saw it at Lambeth it was 'a singular curiosity', but now the fragrant Balm of Gilead is familiar to us all.

His greatest triumph among the trees (or perhaps sharing the honours with his Red Maple and Swamp Cypress) was the one he thought to be a poplar and indeed called 'Populus alba Virginiana Tradescanti, Tradescant's White Virginian Poplar'. It was in fact *Liriodendron tulipifera*, the magnificent tree whose branches in June and July are a garden of tulip-shaped flowers, yellow-green and sometimes other colours. The Tulip Tree caused a sensation when it first flowered at Lambeth. In Virginia it grew in the alluvial plains, on the margins of rivers and on the borders of swamps, liking a deep loamy soil. But it will easily grow on almost any soil, though do not expect it to flower when it is very young. With patience, however, you will be rewarded. The Indians called it the Tree of Peace.

In 1599 Gerard was growing a yucca from the West Indies, which was *Yucca gloriosa*, mistakenly describing it as 'the Roote whereof the bread Casavy or Cazavy is made'. The elder Tradescant was growing a 'Jucca' in 1634. By 1656 John the younger was growing two, one of which was the Virginian *Y. filamentosa*, which almost everyone grows now. It is a dramatic plant with its head of white flowers rising from spiky filamented leaves.

The bergamots give our autumn borders rich glowing reds and purple-tinged flowers. The two best known are *Monarda didyma*, Oswega Tea or Bee Balm, and *M. fistulosa*, the Wild Bergamot. John the younger grew the latter, but as *M. didyma* is regarded as a variety of the other we can say that in effect he introduced both.

Not for a garden where children run about is the Cockspur Thorn – well named, for its thorns are often three inches long! *Crataegus crus-galli* is, however, attractive in leaf, flower and fruit, the latter often staying on into the New Year. It may have been the 'Pyracanthifolia' form which John the younger introduced, for his name for it is 'Pyracantha Virginiana'. This has no thorns, and a mature standard specimen makes a perfect umbrella shape.

From the bizarre genus of the Lords-and-Ladies arums came *Arisaema dracontium* which John called the Great Dragons. Children would love to have a dragon in their garden, and in this case it is a green one, that is to say its spathe or outer shield.

Rather like a penstemon was John's 'Digitalis virginiana angustissimo folio Tradescanti', which he called his 'Narrowest leafed Virginian Foxglove'. But it was *Chelone glabra*, so named because the flower is supposed to look like a tortoise. Its clusters of flowers, white or tinged with rose, grow up the stem, and it is good for the herbaceous border. Another is Prince's Feather (*Amaranthus hypochondriacus*), which grows up to 5ft tall and has flower plumes of deep crimson. John called the plant a 'Flowregentle' and grew three more species than did Gerard who had four.

Now think of your autumn borders without the rich dusky pinks and purples of the phlox. Ours of today are more splendid than *P. paniculata* which John the younger brought back from Virginia, but this was their parent. It had yellow flowers then and was gradually bred through white, rose, and violet-purple, to the rich forms we all know.

To his harvest of border plants he added two exotic fruits: the guava (*Psidium guajava*), seeds of which he collected in Barbados on the way to Virginia, and those of the 'Prickly Costard Apple from Barbados' (*Annona muricata*).

You may ask how all these plants were brought home safely when the journey from Virginia took so many weeks? They were mostly collected as seeds, bulbs or tubers. But I am sure that John could not resist digging up some of them as roots, especially when he found a young sapling he thought he could transport, or a plant just coming into flower – if there were water enough to keep them going on the way home. For it could happen that the journey might be lengthened by a storm that blew the ship miles off course, or the wind could drop and leave them becalmed, or they would lie helpless in a fog. On these occasions water would be rationed to a quart a day. But on the other hand, when a storm blew up and rain sheeted down, it was routine for the seamen to spread a sail along the deck and cup it, when tons of fresh drinking water would be theirs for the catching.

At worst, John would spare some of his ration to keep his plants alive, dampening the moss round them or the matting.

One way and another he succeeded.

The Tradescant story is one of dedication to plants and plant hunting, to gardens and garden design. It was they who made the bridge from the old style of Elizabethan knot garden to the modern garden of ornamental trees, flowering and fruiting shrubs, and interesting flower borders ; who were, moreover, responsible as nurserymen for distributing plants to other gardens.

The story ended tragically. Two years before John the younger visited Virginia for the last time his eighteen-year-old son died. There was now no one to carry on his work or even to add further items of interest to the collection of rarities which was in fact Britain's first public museum.

John the younger died in 1662, at the age of fifty-three; and less than a month later the sinister Elias Ashmole came to claim what he coveted, the world-famous 'Closett of Rarities'. How he had wrung out of John the promise to bequeath the collection jointly to himself and John's widow, Hester, and how he finally wrung it even from her, is another story. He coveted the garden also, and in 1679, a year after he had hounded Hester to her death (drowning herself in the garden pond), he recorded on the eighth and ninth blank pages at the end of John Tradescant's copy of Parkinson's *Paradisus* a list of the 'Trees found in Mrs Tredescants Ground when it came into my possession.' Among them were 'Platinus orientalis verus' and 'Platinus occidentalis, aut Virginensis' which gave birth to the London Plane.

Dr Ducarel was a kindlier occupant of the Tradescants' old house, and in pleading for the restoration of their tomb in St Mary's churchyard, Lambeth, he pointed out to the Royal Society that 'John Tradescant may therefore be justly considered as the earliest collector (in this Kingdom) of every thing that was curious in Natural History, viz. minerals, birds, fishes, insects, &c &c.' and that 'This able man, by his great industry, made it manifest (in the very infancy of botany) that there is scarce any plant extant in the known world, that will not, with proper care, thrive in this kingdom.'

2

DAVID DOUGLAS AND HIS TREES
1799–1834

What are the qualities that go to make up a plant hunter?

He must, of course, have a thorough knowledge of plants of all kinds, be able to identify them not only by their organs of vegetation – root, stem and leaves, and by their organs of reproduction – fruit as well as flower, but know which are new to cultivation and worthy or not of a place in the garden or glasshouse.

This, however, might add up to a scholarly person with no liking for adventure nor toughness to survive it.

David Douglas was tough.

He was born at Scone near Perth on 30 June 1799, the second son of John Douglas, a stonemason; and it is evident that from his earliest years he was a 'handful', for he was not yet four when he was packed off to the village school and not long afterwards (the good dame being likewise unable to control him) removed to the parish school at Kinnoul, which meant walking six miles there and six miles home every day.

This was good training in foot-slogging for the future plant hunter.

Even Kinnoul could not tame him: David much preferred to go fishing or bird-nesting to being penned up with school-books, though at home he would read anything he could get hold of, especially books of travel and adventure, such as

44

Sinbad the Sailor and *Robinson Crusoe*. He was often punished
for not knowing his lessons, and for coming in late or not
coming at all. But no caning affected him so deeply as being
kept in after school hours when the other boys and girls were
set free. David's heart was out in the fields and up in the
hills where he was in his element. He collected all sorts of birds;
hawks and owls being his favourites. Once when raising a nest
of young owls he became skilled in catching mice for them,
and when mice and small birds were exhausted he often spent
his daily lunch penny on bullock's liver for them. He became
expert at fishing, even with a willow-wand for rod, string and
a crooked pin.

A knowledge of the ways of the wild and the ability to hunt
and fish are other resources needful for a plant hunter.

He also collected plants and was fond of gardening, never
needing to be asked to help with weeding, sowing seeds or
thinning the vegetables. This decided his future. His father
asked for a place for him in the Earl of Mansfield's gardens at
Scone Palace, and David was taken on as a garden boy in the
nursery ground. He was then eleven years old, and William
Beattie, the head gardener, observing how well he worked, did
everything he could to encourage and teach him. When David's
independent spirits and mischievous ways led him into quar-
rels with the other boys, their master delivered himself of a
stock reply to their complaints: 'I like a deevil better than a
dult!'

It was a seven-year apprenticeship, and David's first position of responsibility was in the flower garden, where he
learned the names of the plants and the rudiments of botany.
Now in the winter evenings he was to be found deep in his
textbooks: Lee's *Introduction to Botany* and Donn's *Catalogue*,
and any book he could borrow on natural history. His summer
evenings were spent in botanical excursions, when anything
that took his fancy he would bring back to plant in the garden
at home. Interesting visitors would sometimes come to the
Scone Palace garden. Two were the owners of the Perth

Nursery, Robert and J. Brown who every summer went bota-nising in the Highlands. Mr Beattie allowed David to meet them, and he would listen enthralled to their stories of adventure, their descriptions of the romantic scenery of mountain and glen where they had searched for plants. Secretly he resolved that this was what he must do.

He finished his apprenticeship in 1817, and looking remorsefully back to his days of truancy decided to spend the winter at a private school in Perth. The spring of 1818 found him at Valleyfield, near Culross, the seat of Sir Robert Preston. His kind master William Beattie had recommended him to Alexander Stewart, head gardener there, and David was put in charge of some of the exotic plants for which Valleyfield was famous. As at Scone, where he had eagerly learnt all he could about outdoor plants, so David now applied himself to stove plants, proving so good at his work and so anxious to improve his knowledge that he was allowed to use Sir Robert's botanical library. He remained at Valleyfield for two years, having risen to being Alexander Stewart's foreman for the last twelve months.

Now with a working knowledge of indoor and outdoor plants, combined with a botanical knowledge of them, David Douglas applied for a post at the Botanic Garden in Glasgow.

The year was 1820, significant in the history of botany and of gardening, for in April William Jackson Hooker, who was to become the first director of Kew, arrived in Glasgow to take up his appointment as Regius Professor of Botany and have in his charge its Botanic Garden. He found the Garden 'in fine beauty' but the 8,000 species of plants growing in it far too few and its funds at a low ebb. Stewart Murray, the Curator, was delighted when Hooker told him that before he died the great Sir Joseph Banks had made arrangements with Kew, then a royal pleasure ground with Banks its honorary director, for plants which could be 'conveniently spared' to be sent up to Glasgow. Hooker now applied himself to augmenting the plants from every source: other botanic gardens, private

46

gardens and from every part of the world where his students travelled or were based. For in his search for living plants and herbarium material Hooker became known to the leaders of expeditions, to the Lords of the Admiralty, the directors of the Hudson's Bay Company and the chief of the Colonial Office, who in turn were always on the look-out for young botanists and medical men. They could supply the plants, Hooker the graduate doctors who under his brilliant tuition were sound in their botanical knowledge.

So when David Douglas came to Glasgow, it was at that interesting period when new plants were arriving literally by the thousand. Douglas was able to study them in every state, live and as seed, as well as in their dried state on herbarium sheets. He attended Dr Hooker's botanical lectures in the hall of the Garden and became his favourite companion on the famous expeditions to the Highlands where, as Hooker wrote of him, 'his great activity, undaunted courage, singular abstemiousness, and energetic zeal, at once pointed him out as an individual eminently calculated to do himself credit as a scientific traveller'.

So when Joseph Sabine, the Honorary Secretary of the Horticultural Society of London (not yet the Royal) wrote to Hooker asking if he could find him a botanical collector, Hooker at once replied that it was his privilege and that of Mr Murray to recommend Mr Douglas.

David Douglas arrived in London in the spring of 1823, to take up his duties in the career for which he had all along been preparing himself.

The chrysanthemum was a flower arousing everyone's interest at this time. By 1820 the Horticultural Society was growing twelve named kinds, and in the following year Joseph Sabine (who had given them such delightful names as the 'Large Quilled Orange' and the 'Quilled Light Purple') wrote of them: 'They contribute so much to the beauty of our gardens in a fine autumn, and our conservatories in the months of November and December, when scarcely any other plants are in blossom, that they are peculiarly deserving the attention of the ornamental gardener.' Realising that many more were to be discovered, he obtained Council's approval to send one of the Society's young gardeners, John Damper Parks, to China 'to collect, amongst other rarities, as many good varieties of Chrysanthemum as possible'. In fact, it was the Society's intention to send two collectors to China, David Douglas to be the other, but the disturbed state of that country decided them to send only one. Nor were Britain's relations with China very good. In 1816 Lord Amherst had been sent on an embassy to procure better trade terms, but on being presented to the Emperor he indignantly refused to perform the kowtow, declaring that to prostrate himself before a foreign throne would be to lessen the majesty of England. In 1823 he was removed to India.

The Horticultural Society had acquired a new garden at Chiswick the year before, and although there were already 3,000 fruit trees in its orchard the Society was interested in obtaining new ones. The problem of what to do with its newly appointed collector was solved by sending David Douglas to New York with the object of procuring, by gift as far as possible, fruit trees and any other interesting plants and seeds, as well as information on the latest developments in fruit growing.

He left London on 3 June, travelling to Liverpool by coach from Charing Cross, and it was typical of him that while the horses were being changed he should use the time to identify the trees and plants he saw around him and describe them in his diary. The *Ann Maria* of New York was to sail the following morning, and the moment he arrived at Liverpool he made for the Botanic Garden where John Shepherd, the curator, received him 'in the most handsome manner', showing him all his treasures, some of which, Douglas noted, were from North America. Gales, thick rainy weather and mist, then calm and fog delayed progress, and it was not until Sunday 3 August that the ship arrived at Staten Island, New York. Because of smallpox aboard, Douglas was not allowed to take any of his clothes on shore and had to buy new ones. He was now twenty-five years old, having celebrated his birthday on the ship.

His first sight of what America had to offer was on a trip through Staten Island, where oaks and maples were 'growing spontaneously'. He visited some of the finest fruit orchards across the River Hudson, and the Botanic Garden which, sadly, was 'in ruins'. It had been founded as the Elgin Botanic Garden in 1801 when Dr David Hosack, a New Yorker who had finished his medical studies at Edinburgh, become an FRS, FLS and a pupil of James Edward Smith, bought 20 acres of land from New York's City Corporation. Frederick Pursh was in charge of the Garden from 1807 to 1810, in which years it flourished. The rest was a sorry tale: the Garden was transferred to the State of New York under the control of the College of Physicians and Surgeons, then to Columbia University which had not much use for it. For the next half century it was neglected. Hence the 'ruins' which David Douglas saw and deplored.

But Dr Hosack was still active, and when Douglas called on him he started a chain of introductions to nurserymen, botanists and the influential, which kept the visitor busy until December when he sailed back to England with a vast number of boxes full of live and dried plants.

It was certainly a successful trip. There was not a worthwhile nursery, market garden, orchard or even vegetable market that he did not visit in and around New York and its surrounding towns as far as Philadelphia, Wilmington and Newport. He went by stage, steam packet, river boat and on horseback, north to Rochester on Lake Ontario and westwards the length of Lake Erie; and everywhere he went he kept careful notes, gathered seeds, ordered trees and dug up plants. His botanical Bibles were Frederick Pursh's *Flora Americae Septentrionalis* and André Michaux's *North American Sylva*.

Writing his report to Joseph Sabine Douglas mentioned the hasty manner in which he was obliged to travel. It was often a case of being roused early in the morning with the unexpected news that a boat was about to sail for his next destination. Or a kindly acquaintance would suddenly offer a spare seat in his carriage, to take him another fifteen miles on his way. He managed to cover a great deal of ground in the four months of his visit and earn the approbation of the Horticultural Society. He brought back many fine plants and greatly increased the Society's collection of fruits.

Let us see what he found.

Dr Hosack told him about a fine plum named Washington, which was deep yellow marked with crimson and covered with a pale blue bloom. Douglas managed to procure four of the fruits, the largest weighing $3\frac{3}{4}$oz and measuring in circumference $7\frac{3}{8}$in. It became instantly popular when it was raised and distributed in England, being classed as the best after Smith's Orleans, the Greengage and Précon de Tours.

Through Dr Hosack he met Thomas Hogg, an English horticulturist who had emigrated to the USA three years before and set up business in Manhattan as a florist and nurseryman. On 19 August the two set off for Burlington in New Jersey, so that Douglas could visit the orchards of William Coxe. They went by steam packet to New Brunswick, thence by coach to Trenton, and from Trenton to Burlington by steamer.

Coxe was not only one of the foremost fruit growers in America but was distinguished for being the first man there to write on pomology. He received the visitors most hospitably and showed them over his vast orchards in which were growing all the varieties of fruits to be obtained in America with many imported from Europe. He was on the eve of his cider harvest and told Douglas that he would send the Horticultural Society a collection of keeping fruit in the fall.

There were many excursions from New York: to the seedsman David Landreth, another English-born horticulturist, whose business was the leading seed house in America. There Douglas saw a rose new to him. It had been bred in South

Page 51 What would our gardens be without the lilac? John Tradescant the elder found
it in the Mediterranean in 1620 when he was a soldier

Page 52 (left) A house wall glows with the flames of Virginia Creeper, one of the many colourful plants discovered by John the younger

(right) another beautiful plant from the New World, *Hamamelis virginiana*, from which the Wych Hazel of pharmacy is made

Carolina by John Champneys, a wealthy rice planter, and came to be known as Champneys' Pink Cluster or the Champneys Rose. From it Philippe Noisette had raised the original French Noisette rose.

Every day he was picking up new treasures, and he never failed to enter in the diary the plants he saw. But it was not until Tuesday 16 September, when he was at Amherstberg on Lake Erie, that he wrote: 'This is what I might term my first day in America. The trees in the woods were of astonishing magnitude ... '

It was the oaks that captivated him, and to Joseph Sabine he wrote a special account of them, telling him: 'Their number and beauty and the acknowledged utility of their wood, particularly attracted my attention, and of the thirty-four species enumerated by Pursh as natives of the vast continent of North America, I was so fortunate as to meet with no less than nineteen.' Only two of them were new to England when he brought them home as acorns to be raised by the Horticultural Society – *Quercus catesbaei* and *Quercus garryana* – but it proved one thing: David Douglas was a man of the trees.

So pleased was the Horticultural Society with the results of this mission that it decided to send him to America again the following year, this time to explore the botanical riches of the North West adjoining the Columbia River and southwards towards California. The Hudson's Bay Company had offered him the opportunity of travelling with its agents into remote regions hitherto untrodden by any naturalist, and in his *Sketch of a Journey to the North Western Parts of the Continent of North America During the Years 1824, 5, 6, and 7* Douglas prefaces the account of his adventures by giving his grateful thanks to John Henry Pelly, Governor of the Hudson's Bay Company and to Nicholas Garry, Deputy Governor, for whom Douglas in 1828 was to name the delightful evergreen shrub of long grey-green catkins *Garrya elliptica*. He named for him also the oak of that epithet, as 'a sincere though simple token of gratitude'.

Douglas sailed on Sunday 25 July in the Company's brig *William and Ann*, destined for the entrance of the River Columbia. He was delighted to find on board Dr John Scouler, a fellow pupil of their mutual friend Dr Hooker who had recommended Scouler as surgeon to the vessel.

The Panama Canal did not come into being for another century, so their route was round Cape Horn with Funchal their first port of call. Here with two days to spend ashore Douglas and his companion went botanising, finding several interesting plants but no new ones. During the long monotonous voyage Douglas kept his interest in natural history alive by observing the sea birds and flying fish, and in making paper bags for collecting seeds. On reaching Rio de Janeiro he called on John Dickson, a surgeon with the Royal Navy and friend of Joseph Sabine. Through him he met William Harrison, a Liverpool man who had introduced many interesting plants to the Botanic Gardens there. He had a fine garden of his own five miles from town at Botafogo, where on an old wall were about seventy species of epidendrum and orchid growing on the original branches or stumps on which he had found them. These were nailed to the wall and the plants were obviously thriving. Both Dickson and Harrison gave him introductions to their friends, and he met Mrs Maria Grahame who was tutor to the young daughter of the newly crowned Brazilian emperor, Pedro I. Mrs Grahame was full of information about the natural history of Chile and Brazil, and Douglas was delighted with her descriptions of the plants around Valparaíso and Juan Fernández. In his walks near the city he recognised many of the plants cultivated in England, puny in their exiled state but here luxuriant.

The island of Juan Fernández was rewarding. During his short stay in what he called 'the Madeira of the South' Douglas collected seventy distinct and interesting plants for his herbarium, and at Cruz Bay he sowed a quantity of garden seeds.

They reached the Galapagos Islands on Sunday 9 January 1825, and it was after leaving James's Island that a calamity happened, the first of many that were to plague David Douglas throughout the next nine years: he lost almost all the many plants and birds he had collected, because of the incessant rains that lasted for twelve days. His plants, eighty-nine of them, had not been sufficiently dry to pack away. One was a Filmy Fern which he had found in a deep shady ravine on Juan Fernández. He remembered the carpet of it growing close by a crystal rill chinkling and cascading down through the rugged hills, and how he had lain down on it, among the deliciously veined and crisped foliage.

He landed on the banks of the Columbia River in the spring, eight months and fourteen days after leaving England. He was to remain in the district for the next two years, sending home plants, seeds and herbarium material in such abundance and of such rich variety that the Horticultural Society was amazed. On this trip alone he was to collect 800 species of which more than 200 were to prove new introductions.

His first important discoveries were at Cape Disappointment at the entrance to the Columbia, where the ship anchored 'after a comparitively [sic] tedious voyage' (though they had suffered all that the sea could offer in the way of boisterous weather with high seas, thunderstorms, hail, fog, rain and calms). 'On stepping on the shore *Gaultheria shallon* was the first plant I took in my hands. So pleased was I that I could scarcely see anything but it,' Douglas wrote excitedly. We know it as a valuable evergreen windbreak producing sprays of pink flowers in May and June. The handsome bramble *Rubus spectabilis* was abundant and in bright magenta-rose flower. *Arbutus menziesii*, the noble Madrona Tree, was another discovery here. It was one of Douglas's finest introductions and has proved hardy in the Home Counties.

On the south side of the river the ground was low and thickly wooded with pines, 'one of which,' Douglas guessed, 'may prove to be *Pinus taxifolia*.' It proved to be *Pseudotsuga douglasii*, later named *P. menziesii* because it had originally been discovered by Archibald Menzies who sailed with Vancouver, but which Douglas introduced. The Oregon Douglas Fir is one of our stateliest conifers.

His base was Fort Vancouver, a place sublime for its scenery of high well-wooded hills rising to the grandeurs of Mounts Hood, St Helen, Vancouver and Jefferson, white with perpetual snow. Below them, the meadows and plains were lush with grass and flowering plants.

In the next months his labours were well rewarded by *Ribes sanguineum*, the American Flowering Currant whose crimson tassels delight us on bleak March days; *Mahonia aquifolium*, called the Oregon Grape, of dense yellow racemes in spring followed by decorative blue-black berries; the lustrous *Mahonia nervosa*, turning red in the autumn; *Acer microphyllum*, the Oregon Maple, with leaves turning bright orange; *Lonicera ciliosa*, the western Trumpet Honeysuckle of long yellow flowers tinged with purple; the violet-blue spikes of *Camassia esculenta* and, as Douglas wrote, 'a multitude of other plants', adding: 'I cannot pass over the grandeur of *Lupinus polyphyllus* covering immense tracts of low land on the banks of streams, with here and there a white variety.' This beautiful plant, growing 6–8ft tall where it was partly overflowed by water, was another parent of our border lupin (John Tradescant had introduced *L. perennis*). In all, David Douglas introduced twenty-three different species of lupin.

Towards the end of June he availed himself of a river boat going to the Hudson's Bay Company's trading posts in the interior. He botanised along the banks until they passed the Grand Rapids, when for the next seventy miles the banks were steep and rocky. Then gradually the hills fell away, the trees thinned to stumpy timber until the scene was one dreary waste of barren soil. Yet it was here that he found the beautiful *Clarkia pulchella* of lilac-coloured and white flowers, and *Calochortus macrocarpus* with its nodding lavender bells, and two more lupins – the purple-blue *Lupinus aridus* and the varicoloured

56

L. leucophyllus – which he identified by their leaves, as they were not in flower, and whose seeds he was to collect later. The river was low and he could not go higher than a few miles above the falls. But he was amply repaid by finding the yellow-flowered shrubby *Purshia tridentata*, the easily grown annual *Collomia grandiflora* whose yellow flowers turn red, and, as he noted, 'several Pentstemons'. Again, David Douglas was to be famed for his introduction of these last lovely flowers: he gave us nineteen different species, naming one *Penstemon scouleri* after his shipboard companion. This is a gem for the rock garden, forming prostrate clumps and mats of bright green foliage with rose-purple flowers. What faithful flowers the penstemons are, in bloom from July till the end of the year.

In the middle of July he began his descent of the river in an Indian canoe, intending to continue his searches on the coast. This plan was hampered by the tribe with whom he was living going to war with the natives inhabiting the district through which he had to pass. Cockqua, the chief of the village, looked after him like a father and was so concerned for his guest's safety that he himself kept watch over Douglas throughout the night on which he expected the enemy to raid them. In the evening about 300 men executed a war-dance and sang death-songs. The following day nearly 400 warriors joined them, and only after several harangues were hostilities suspended. Douglas arrived back at Fort Vancouver on 6 August and employed himself for the next fortnight in drying his plants and making short journeys in quest of seeds, adding them to those of *Holodiscus discolor* var. *ariifolius* which with others he had collected on the way down the river. This handsome spiraea-like shrub with creamy-white panicles of flowers in July is well worth growing. It is much like *H. discolor* itself, which is generally credited to David Douglas as an 1827 introduction.

He set off again on 19 August, this time up the Multnomah, a southern tributary of the Columbia, in three days reaching the village of the Calapooie Indians. An excursion to the plains

brought him *Eschscholzia californica* var. *douglasii* whose pure
yellow flowers are now a delight of our gardens; *Iris tenax* of
claret flowers, and a new nicotiana (*N. quadrivalvia* var. *multi-
valvis*). It was the friendly habit of the Indians to pass round
their tobacco pouches when the day's work was over, and in
one of them Douglas found the seeds of a large pine tree, which
they ate as nuts. He learned that these pines grew in the mountains to the south, but alas, when he found them, none of the
seeds was perfect. He had to wait two years before he was
rewarded, and this was the introduction of another David
Douglas conifer, *Pinus lambertiana*, the Sugar Pine, the largest
of all in its native habitat, in Britain a medium-sized tree of long
pendulous cones, with beautiful brown shoots in the winter.

There was time for only two more trips before winter set in.
On 5 September, accompanied by a Canadian and some Indian
guides, Douglas left for the Grand Rapids, and from this
journey we learn something of the hardships he endured. He
wanted to reach the summits of the mountains on the north
side of the river, but when he explained this to Chumtalia his
chief guide promptly went sick and sent a younger brother
instead. Douglas left the Canadian in charge of his valuables,
his seeds and notes, and had to encourage his guides by giving
them the whole of the provisions on the first day, except four
small biscuits and a little tea and sugar. At their first encampment, about two-thirds of the way up the mountain, they left
their blankets, intending to return and sleep there after having
reached the summit, but their path being so dreadfully fatigu-
ing, climbing over shelving rocks and fallen timber, night
closed in before they could reach it. Douglas killed a young
brown eagle and they made their supper of it, with a little tea
brewed in an open kettle and drunk out of bark dishes. They
got back to camp in the dusk of the following evening, Douglas
faint and weak from the violent exertion. His feet were in a
bad state and it was two days before he could set out again.

This time Chumtalia consented to go with him, even although it meant ascending a mountain on the south side of the

river. They reached the top after a laborious climb of 15 hours, and here Douglas had the good fortune to find two new species of pine: *Abies nobilis*, the Noble Fir, of huge upstanding cones and soft saxe-blue foliage, in maturity 'heightened to silvery whiteness'; and *Abies amabilis*, the Red Silver Fir, whose foliage of the darkest and most lustrous green is streaked underneath with two silver bands. His collection of pines was mounting up. He also added the seeds of several new penstemons, and there were interesting species of *Ribes*. David Douglas was responsible for introducing no fewer than thirteen different kinds of these shrubs with their ornamental and useful scarlet, black, and purple fruits.

On his return to Fort Vancouver he packed his gleanings for despatch: twenty-four large bundles of dried plants, a large chest of seeds, one of birds and animals he had collected, and one of various articles of Indian dress. These he intended to take down to the Company's ship, due to arrive at Whitby Harbour, but unfortunately a fall on a rusty nail brought up a large abscess on his left knee, and regretfully he had to write a note to the ship's captain, asking him to place his boxes where they would be kept aired, particularly the chest of seeds. For ten days he nursed his knee, and then on hearing joyfully that the ship had been detained by contrary winds, which meant that he could after all see that the boxes were properly placed on board, he left Fort Vancouver with Alexander McKenzie, who was one of the Company's men, a small canoe and four Indians.

Bad luck dogged them all the way. First, a violent westerly wind kept them hugging the north shore of the river; then the canoe struck a tree and was ripped from end to end. It was days before it was repaired, and when they arrived at Tongue Point it was to find that they had missed the ship by just one hour. Douglas was bitterly disappointed, for he had hoped to see John Scouler before he left for England. He spent the night at the lodge of one of the Chenook chiefs who begged the Grass Man, as the Indians called Douglas, to let his brother travel with him. The following morning Com-Comly, the Chief of all the Chenooks on the north side of the river, sent his own canoe with twelve Indians to ferry them across the Columbia to Baker's Bay. Midstream a violent storm overtook them and they lost all their provisions. Throughout the next day the rain fell in torrents. Twice they were obliged to shift their camp because of the rising tide; and with no food they resorted to eating the roots of arrowhead and lupins. 'From continual exposure to the cold and rain and the want of proper subsistence I became greatly reduced,' the Grass Man wrote in his journal. Sixty miles up the River Cheeheelie, with continual rain and signs of approaching winter, they gave up their intention of going to the river's source, deciding to travel overland to the River Cow-a-lidsk, another tributary of the Columbia. Though not more than forty miles distant, it took them two days to reach it, and now all the food they had to eat were the berries poor Douglas had so painstakingly collected to send home. Seeds of the grassy-leaved *Helonias tenax* (*Xerophyllum tenax*), *Rubus spectabilis*, which was his introduction, and a few others were the only things he saved on this unfortunate journey.

It was not until March 1826 that he was able to resume plant hunting, when Dr John McLoughlin, Chief Factor of the Hudson's Bay Company, allowed him to embark in the spring boat for the interior. He gave him thirty quires of paper (weighing 102lb) for drying his plants, 'which was an enormous indulgence', though to carry such a weight Douglas had to cut down even his small supply of clothing. He set off on Monday the 20th in the company of Francis Ermatinger and John M'Leod who was going to Hudson's Bay, with two boats and fourteen men. They reached the Falls on the 24th, the first stage of Douglas's journey to the country skirting the Rocky Mountains, where he hoped to spend the spring season.

The scenery was magnificent, the high mountains covered with huge pines whose lofty wide-spreading branches were loaded with snow. At the Grand Rapids a rainbow arched across the cloud of vapour hanging above the churning waters. But danger awaited them. Reaching the lower part of the Great Falls they were pestered by Indians demanding tobacco. There were at least 450 of them, and the night was spent in keeping watch. Douglas lit a few of his small wax tapers and by their light wrote to his friend Stewart Murray of the Glasgow Botanic Garden, and arranged the mosses he had been collecting. He was sometimes very lonely, so that to write a letter home was like talking to a friend. Letters received were read over and over again. His one constant companion was his dog, 'my old terrier, a most faithful, and now, to judge from his long grey beard, venerable friend, who has guarded me throughout my journeys, and whom, should I live to return, I mean certainly to pension off on four pennyworth of cat's-meat per day!'

They took a hurried breakfast by the boats, at the Great Falls hearing that more Indians were lying in wait for them. The warning proved correct. An arrow was aimed at M'Leod, and but for Douglas's quick action in levelling his gun at the warrior and the intervention of a chief of the Kyemuse tribe and three of his young men, they would have been in serious trouble. Douglas rewarded the chief with the only coin he possessed, a shilling which had been in his pocket ever since he left London.

There was no sleep that night. Douglas used the anxious hours in writing to Dr Hooker, confessing to him that he should have sailed home by the boat which took his last consignment of plants, these being Mr Sabine's orders, but that, instead, he hoped that his going to the Rocky Mountains would result in a most splendid collection.

By 5 June he had three large bundles of select plants and more than forty varieties of seeds. Among the latter were those of his lovely rose-purple *Penstemon scouleri* and the thornless Salmon Berry (*Rubus parviflorus*) of downy palmate leaves, white flowers and large red fruits; three currants, and a new species of pine, *P. ponderosa*, the Western Yellow Pine. Growing on this tree was a mistletoe belonging to a distinct race inhabiting pine trees and some other conifers.

One of his most exciting finds was *Paeonia brownii*, whose dark maroon flowers cupped a golden disc. It was the first ever found in America. Douglas discovered it in the Blue Mountains on the verge of the eternal snow where no white man had trod before. Lower down, whole slopes of the mountain were covered with the beautiful golden lupin he named after Joseph Sabine. And everywhere he went he found a new penstemon: on the clay hills above Okanagan, *P. glaber* of bright blue and purple flowers; in the Blue Mountains, the violet and lilac *P. glandulosus*; on his descent of the Spokane River the yellow-white flowers of *P. deustus*.

He travelled as boats and guides were available, or when horses were provided, as when John W. Dease lent him three of his best horses and two hunters to go to Spokane, seventy miles from the Kettle Falls. He came down the Spokane River with William Kitson to collect on the plains. He attached himself to a party commanded by Archibald McDonald and John Worth, so that he could visit Lewis and Clarke's River. Finally, having spent the first half of August collecting seeds of all the important plants he had seen earlier in the Kettle Falls area, he descended the whole chain of the river from the Kettle Falls to the sea, a distance of 800 miles and losing all his provisions when his canoe was swamped, losing the canoe itself when it was wrecked in the dangerous rapids below the Great Falls, with a collection of insects, his pistols, and some seeds. Fifteen miles above the Grand Rapids he walked to the home of his old guide Chumtalia who took him in his own canoe to Fort Vancouver. He arrived there at 4 o'clock on the morning of 30 August, and next day packed his plants and seeds for despatch to England.

Now he was going to northern California, one of a party of

thirty under the command of A. R. McLeod. They proceeded up the River Multnomah and at the Company's encampment collected horses for the next stage of their journey, which was south-west, at first through fertile wooded country abounding with streams, plains and belts of oak. October came in clear and dry, with cool misty evenings, but late as the season was there were many curious and beautiful plants to be found. 'Princely' was the tree he was delighted to find as they crossed a hill 2,500ft above its platform of foothills. It was *Castanopsis chrysophylla*, whose leaves had a dark rich red glossiness on the upper surface and were rich golden-yellow beneath. Some of the specimens were 60–100ft tall. 'Nothing,' wrote Douglas, 'can exceed the magnificence of this tree, or the strikingly beautiful contrast formed with the sable glory of the shadowy pine among which it delights to grow.' It was on 9 October 1826 that he stood admiring it, when the prickly balls of its nuts would be ripe. The introduction date is given as 1848. Later, we shall learn why.

Mid-October found them riding down the banks of the Red Deer River, a tributary of the Umpqua, and here Douglas discovered the beautiful evergreen shrub called the Californian Laurel or Sassafras (*Umbellularia californica*), later on the journey being treated by the Indians to a feast of their nuts, roasted in the embers of their camp fire, as an accompaniment to salmon trout.

Now came days of hard going, dreary with rain and hail, at night loud with thunder. He had hoped to find perfect cones of his *Pinus lambertiana*, and now, crossing a low hill, he came upon the trees, immensely grand and with long straight trunks unbranched for two-thirds of their height. Some of the trees were over 200ft tall, but the cones were easily visible, hanging like sugar loaves from the ends of the branches. Douglas was successfully harvesting them by shooting them down with his gun, when eight Indians, painted with red earth and armed with bows and arrows, bone-tipped spears and flint knives, came from among the trees. They looked anything but friendly, and it was only by a ruse that Douglas escaped and got back to his camp with three of the precious cones in his pocket.

Look at a physical map of Oregon. See the brown stretches indicating mountainous country. No wonder that the poor horses, having clambered for days over hills strewn with fallen timber, were 'worn down to the greatest extremity'. Douglas himself had little zeal to continue. The hostility of the Indians, the unpleasant rains and the lateness of the season which now could bring him little more, decided him to make for the sea, there to await the arrival of Mr McLeod who with his party had gone to the south. They met there on 4 November, and as the agent was sending two men to Columbia Douglas decided to return with them : he was not well enough equipped to spend the winter in the woods.

It was a twelve days' march in great misery, hunger, rain and cold. But what was heart-breaking to Douglas was the almost total loss of his collections when crossing the River Sandiam. Which explains why the introductions of David Douglas's Golden Chestnut – his 'princely tree', and others, have a later date than 1826.

On Tuesday 20 March 1827 the Hudson's Bay Company's 'annual express' set off from Fort Vancouver on a journey across the North American continent that was to end five months later at Hudson Bay itself. Douglas, who was homeward bound, was taking this opportunity of exploring new terrain. His companion this time was Edward Ermatinger, and for part of the way Dr John McLoughlin, the Chief Factor, who was going to the interior with A. R. McLeod and two others of his men. They followed the rivers : the whole chain of the Columbia to the Rocky Mountains, the Athabasca to Fort Assiniboine, the Saskatchewan to Lake Winnipeg, travelling by canoe almost the entire way.

The route was familiar to Douglas as far as the Rockies. But, even so, he found plants that were new. *Fritillaria pudica*

64

was one of his introductions, which he had seen the previous year, the only plant in blossom on the plains below Lewis and Clarke's River, beautiful with its long golden-yellow and orange bells tinged with purple. Now he gathered its bulbs. Whenever possible, if he could keep pace with the boats, he botanised along the banks, taking a single specimen of each plant not already sent to England. At Fort Colville on the Kettle Falls of the Columbia he packed them, writing to Joseph Sabine that the Hudson's Bay Company's ship had arrived and that he had put on board four boxes for the Horticultural Society, containing all the plants he had so far collected in North-west America. It was here that he bade farewell to John McLoughlin and A. R. McLeod, leaving them at 9 o'clock to be conveyed to his camp a mile above the establishment, ready for an early start the next morning with his own contingent: Edward Ermatinger whom he found a most agreeable young man, four Canadians and three Iriquois Indians.

It was snowing when they set off at daylight. Next day *Erythronium grandiflorum* fell to his trowel: it was in full flower of bright yellow with an orange base. That evening he wished with all his heart he could have painted what he saw, for at sunset the snowy summits of the hills were tinted with gold, and in the blue shadows the pines wove darker blues and greens, while stealing along the base of the hills the river was all silvery brightness. 'When you get home, begin to learn,' the would-be artist exhorted himself.

At the head of the Columbia Douglas varied his journey by climbing up one of the Cascade Mountains, choosing the highest. The going was laborious, and even wearing snow-shoes he kept sinking up to his middle. Half-way up it was easier, as he was walking on a hard crust. One-third from the summit it became a peak of pure ice. The ascent took him five hours, the descent only an hour and a quarter, for taking off his snow-shoes and tying them together he made a toboggan of them and was able to sledge down 500 or 700ft in a minute and a half. He was glad to get back to camp, for the scenery was frightening, mountain upon mountain and rugged beyond description, with snow and ice falls producing crashes and awful grumblings like the shock of an earthquake, the echo of which would cannon round the valley for several minutes. In gratitude to the two botanists he most revered, he named his peak Mount Brown after Robert Brown who was now Keeper of the Botany Department of the British Museum, and a peak a little to the south and nearly the same height Mount Hooker in honour of his early patron, 'to whose kindness, I, in a great measure, owe my success hitherto in life'.

There were the usual hardships on the way, hostile Indians to be avoided and hunger to be endured, and a desperate encounter with a wounded wild bull that gave chase to Finan McDonald, one of his party, and gored him terribly. It was Finan McDonald who gave us the description of Douglas as 'a sturdy little Scot, handsome rather, with a head and face of a fine Grecian mould; of winning address, and withal the most pious of men'.

July greeted them with thunderstorms, high winds and rain, but Douglas went on gleaning plants, no fewer than 291 of all kinds by the time he reached Lake Winnipeg. The remainder of his journey to York Factory on Hudson Bay was uneventful, despite the fact that when descending a rapid his boat struck heavily on a rock and shattered seven of its timbers and planking. His herbarium papers were drenched, but he managed to dry them, and three treasures he had planted in a small box (his Erythronium, his Fritillaria and a Claytonia) survived in good condition. His own person looked the worse for wear when he arrived at York Factory, to be welcomed by John George McTavish and presented with a new suit of clothes which the Chief Factor had thoughtfully had made for him. In the *Prince of Wales* he took farewell of Hudson Bay on 15 September and arrived at Portsmouth a month later.

A tremendous welcome awaited him in London. He found himself a hero, fêted and admired. The Linnean Society elected him a Fellow. Never before had any collector introduced so many hardy and ornamental plants. (Birds and animals, too. The Zoological and Geographical Societies gave him honorary membership.) Indeed, the botanical world was 'literally startled by the number and importance of his discoveries'. His *Ribes sanguineum* was considered to be 'of such importance to the embellishment of our gardens, that', as John Lindley wrote, 'if the expense incurred by the Horticultural Society in Mr Douglas's voyage had been attended with no other result than the introduction of this species, there would have been no ground for dissatisfaction'. The cost of this remarkable expedition was less than £400.

For a time Douglas enjoyed the lionising, though he was 'the shyest being almost that I ever saw', as Thomas Andrew Knight, the Horticultural Society's President, described him; and soon he became bored and irritable, hating the life and climate of London and yearning to be back in the wilds. It was not long before he was suggesting to the Society that he should be sent on another expedition, this time to California where a whole world of new plants awaited discovery. It took nearly two years to convince the Society that the day of the plant hunter was not over, and meanwhile Douglas began to prepare his journals for publication, a task he found uncongenial and never finished. He worked on his herbarium, and at the Chiswick garden superintended the propagation of his plants. (So vast were the quantities of seeds he had sent, that the Society had great difficulty in distributing them.) Because of his knowledge of North-western America he was called in to advise the Oregon Boundary Commission, and he went to Greenwich to study geographical observation and surveying under Joseph Sabine's brother, Captain Edward Sabine.

Then in 1829 the Society's Council decided to let him travel again. But not to California. He was to make a wider exploration of the same districts as before. He was also to utilise his training as a surveyor. The Colonial Office kitted him out with the necessary instruments: barometers, thermometer, chronometer and hygrometer. His map of the River Columbia is still considered among the best. On 31 October, after paying a farewell visit to his mother at Scone, David Douglas sailed to America for the third and last time. He was never again to see the shores of England.

After the long Atlantic voyage his ship, the *Eagle*, remained for a month at the Sandwich Islands where the tropical vegetation fascinated Douglas: the Tree Ferns, the timber trees festooned with creepers and species of tillandsia. He made up his mind to return some day to make a proper study of it all.

On 3 June the ship reached the Columbia, and he was greeted by the news that it would be inadvisable to proceed inland because of tribal warfare going on among the Indians. Not only this: fever was decimating their villages. So he cooled his heels for several weeks, collecting where he could, and then decided to make for his old hunting-grounds at the head of Lewis and Clarke's River. The trip, involving '60 days of severe fatigue', was rewarding for himself and the Horticultural Society: three chests of seeds which he despatched by the *Eagle* when she sailed for home in mid-October. With the seeds went a bundle of six species ('exceedingly beautiful', Douglas wrote) of the genus *Pinus*. 'Among these, *P. nobilis* is by far the finest. I spent three weeks in a forest composed of this tree, and day by day could not cease to admire it; in fact, my words can only be monotonous expressions of this feeling.' He had added another new species during this journey, *grandis*, the Giant Fir of long bright green cones and fragrant foliage. Both these are now classed under *Abies*.

He thought now of California, which then belonged to Mexico; but so long did it take to procure permits to travel and botanise, that the Californian spring (which had already begun when he reached Monterey on 22 December) was almost over by the time he could go on any but local excursions. After that, Douglas made the most of his time, and sent back to England such a wealth of new plants that the Horticultural Society could not have wished him elsewhere than travelling about his unbotanised land. Thus came to Britain such now-familiar

Page 69
An autumn border of Michaelmas Daisies which with the first lupins and phloxes were introduced from Virginia

Page 70 Many Scots have made brave plant hunters. David Douglas was one of them; in his travels in North America he lived with the Indians, who called him the 'Grass Man'

garden plants as the deep rich yellow eschscholzia, the elegant clarkia, the charming Butter-and-Eggs (*Limnanthes douglasii*) of white and yellow flowers beloved by bees, mimuluses, and so many new pine trees that he wrote to Dr Hooker: 'You will begin to think that I manufacture Pines at my pleasure!' These were the Monterey Pine (*P. radiata*), the Big-Cone Pine (*P. coulteri*), the Sitka Spruce (*Picea sitchensis*) which is now one of our most important afforestation trees, the Western White Pine (*Pinus monticola*) whose shape is a tall narrow pyramid, and *P. sabiniana*, the Digger Pine, which Douglas had originally discovered in 1826 and named after his patron at the Horticultural Society. The cones gathered then were among the seeds and plants which he lost with his notes when crossing a rapid stream.

At Monterey he had been kindly received by the monks, and they had helped him explore the immediate countryside. Now, just as he had been afforded the facilities of the Hudson's Bay Company's trading posts, he stopped at the Roman Catholic missions all the way south, down the Salinas Valley to Santa Barbara. You can still trace his route on the map: Nuestra Sen de la Soledad, San Antonio de Padua, San Miguel Archangel, San Luis Obisko des Tolosa, La Purissima Concepción, and Santa Inez Virgen y Martyr. Douglas could speak no Spanish, but he was able to converse with the monks in Latin.

He reached Santa Barbara in the middle of May and returned to Monterey late in June by the same route, occasionally penetrating the mountain valleys skirting the coast. Shortly afterwards he started for San Francisco, intending to reach the spot where he had been in 1826, but the intervening sixty-five miles proved too much for him. He wrote to Dr Hooker that his year's collection amounted to 500 species, 'a little more or less. This is vexatiously small, I am aware; but when I inform you that the season for botanising does not last longer than three months, your surprize will cease. Such is the rapidity with which Spring advances, as on the table lands of Mexico and the platforms of the Andes in Chile, the plants bloom here only

E

for a day. The intense heat sets in about June when every bit of herbage is dried to a cinder.' Still, of new genera he was certain there were nineteen or twenty at least, and he hoped that Dr Hooker would find many more. As for species, he thought about 340 might be new.

What impressed Douglas most in California was the great beauty of the redwoods. He called them a species of *Taxodium*, which was the old name. We know this magnificent tree, the tallest in the world, as *Sequoia sempervirens*. Douglas could hardly believe their height and repeatedly measured them. A few he saw were upwards of 300ft tall. 'I possess fine specimens and seeds also,' he told Dr Hooker. These he sent to England, but perhaps the seed did not remain viable, for it is Carl Theodor Hartweg who is credited with their introduction in 1843.

Douglas was awaiting a ship from the Columbia, and decided that should she not arrive before 10 December he would take a passage in an American vessel for the Sandwich Islands, and proceed to the north-west coast the following spring. Neither ship arrived, and he contented himself with spending another season in California, telling Dr Hooker that he would consider it 'as new to me'. From various excursions to the interior he brought back what he called 'a host of new and beautiful plants'. One was the spurred *Delphinium cardinale* of long many-flowered racemes bright red and yellow. There were seven undescribed *Calochortus*, the bulbous plant related to the tulip and fritillary. Called the Mariposa Lily or Globe Tulip or Star Tulip, its grassy leaves support beautiful hanging bells or starry cups at the end of a graceful neck. The species *albus*, *luteus*, the lilac *splendens*, the crimson *venustus* and *pulchellus* of bright yellow globes were all his. There were three phacelias, including the one we all know as the Wild Heliotrope (*tanacetifolia*). There was a 'multitude' of oenotheras, seven new lupins, and that wonderful annual *Nemophila menziesii*, popularly called Baby Blue Eyes, with its climbing cousin of purple-violet flowers, *N. aurita*.

These were only some of the plants resulting from his twelve months' stay in California, for in August 1832 he was off to the Sandwich Islands at last, and there he shipped his Californian collections by the *Sarah and Elizabeth*: nineteen large bundles of dried plants in two chests, with seeds and specimens of timber. They were addressed to the Horticultural Society of London – 'should such exist', Douglas wrote parenthetically to Dr Hooker, for he had heard that the Society was in financial difficulties. But he did not connect this with the news he heard on leaving the Islands, that his friend and patron had resigned the secretaryship. Imagining that Joseph Sabine had somehow been unfairly treated or disgraced, Douglas immediately resigned his appointment as collector, though he continued for the next year to send his plants as usual. There were not many from the Sandwich Islands. Most of his time had been spent in bed, in agonies of rheumatic fever. In October he was back at Fort Vancouver, and before winter closed in he made an excursion north of the Columbia to New Georgia where he collected mosses and seaweeds. In March he followed the course of the Columbia, finding the first flowers of spring. Among them was a new species of phlox, *P. longifolia* of rosy corymbs.

He wrote to Dr Hooker in April, saying that in a few days he would be travelling northward. He would go by canoe or on horseback, but mainly on foot. It was into mountainous country where, said the Indians, not even a deer came, save once in a hundred years. And to his kind friend he confessed that the sight of his right eye was gone. The trouble had started with an attack of ophthalmia in 1826, followed by snow-blindness. The scorching heat of California had put paid to it. He now used purple-tinted goggles to diminish the glare of the snow, 'though most reluctantly, as every object, plants and all, is thus rendered of the same colour'. But he was in excellent spirits, and the sight of his remaining eye had become infinitely more delicate and clear. Indeed, one of his companions had particularly remarked on his power of vision, his quickness to discover any small object or plant even on the river bank as they travelled along in the boat.

On 13 June disaster befell Douglas. At the Stony Islands his canoe was dashed to pieces and he lost every article in his possession except an astronomical journal, a book of rough notes, some charts, and barometrical observations and instruments. His botanical notes were lost and his journal. Worse still, his collection of plants of about 400 species. It was hardly any consolation that he himself was saved. He was swept over the cataract into the whirlpool below and was washed by the waves on to the rocks. The loss of his plants almost defeated him, but with determination and courage he set himself the task of collecting replacements. Dr Hooker had been sending him the parts of his *Flora Boreali-Americana* as they were published, and Douglas hoped that he had some good species for describing in the next issue, hoped indeed that he could present them to him in person, as he was coming back to England.

His route was the same as that of the outgoing voyage, via the longed-for Sandwich Islands. He reached Hawaii on 2 January 1834. The view of the island from the sea was sublime, combining, as he wrote, 'the grand, sweet, and beautiful, in the most remarkable degree'. Above the bluest of seas rose the mountains, rich with bananas, sugar-cane, coffee, pandanus and bread-fruit for the first 2,500ft, for the next 8,000ft thickly timbered. Above this was short verdure for another 3,700ft, after which the mountains were bare.

On 7 January Douglas set off to climb the 13,796ft high Mouna Kuah (Mauna Kea) with Honoré, his guide and interpreter, and sixteen men – five to carry his luggage and provisions, and eleven to carry their own *tapas* and food (they ate enormously, consuming two bullocks in a week, besides what they carried). The mountain was of volcanic origin, as indeed are the Sandwich Islands themselves, Mauna Kea being the largest volcano in the world and the scene of many terrible eruptions. It was no small undertaking to reach the top, crawling over lava ridges where sometimes the ground beneath his feet was the thinnest of crusts covering the boiling subterranean fires; in the jungle-like glens between the ridges, wading

74

through seas of mud. On the second morning he accomplished only seven miles. Not only was the path difficult, he was carrying more than 6olb on his back, mainly his surveying instruments and drying-papers. But on this stage of the climb he had a pleasant companion in a Mr Miles who was part-owner of the sawmill he had passed the day before. Miles was on his way up the mountain to join his partner whose job was to cure the flesh of the wild cattle roaming near the verge of the wood. From him Douglas learnt that the grassy flank of the mountain abounded with these cattle, which were offspring of stock left here by Captain Vancouver. They were now proving of very great benefit to the island. Deep pits covered with branches were the means of trapping them.

The mountain yielded Douglas an interesting harvest. He found growing on the highest reaches of vegetation a gigantic composite later named by Hooker *Argyrophytum douglasii* (*Argyroxiphium sandwichense*) which had a column of sharp pointed leaves densely covered with silvery threads. At the end of his fourteen days' excursion his collection amounted to several bundles of plants, large packets tied up in coa baskets made from a beautiful acacia tree whose timber resembled mahogany. Nearly fifty species of fern were added on the way down.

The island has another volcanic mountain, Mauna Loa, of almost equal height, and this Douglas also explored, delighting again in the tropical plants, though the maura trees in full blossom reminded him of English laburnums. Faithfully he was still keeping his journal, each evening writing a full account of the day's events. The last entry is dated 6 May, when Douglas had arrived at Kapupala, taking barometer readings at 8 pm and reporting the sky clear.

What happened on 12 May is told in the sad letter the missionaries of Hawaii sent to Richard Charlton, the British Consul. Douglas, accompanied by a guide, had left Rohala Point to cross Mauna Loa on the north side. On the way he had dismissed his guide, who had warned him to be very careful lest he fall into a bull pit. They had passed one only a few minutes before, and others were two miles ahead. Later that day the body of David Douglas was found at the bottom of one of them, terribly mangled by an enraged bull. The little terrier who always went with him was found nearby, faithfully guarding the bundle Douglas had been carrying. Had curiosity tempted him to take a fatal step too near the edge of the pit? It will never be known.

What is certain is that Douglas was one of the greatest plant hunters who has ever lived. On the centenary of his first mission to North-west America the *Gardeners Chronicle* reminded its readers: 'There is scarcely a spot deserving the name of garden, either in Europe or in the United States, in which some of the discoveries of Douglas do not form the chief attraction. The frequent mention of his name as the discoverer and introducer of some of the finest coniferous trees that adorn the lawns and parks of Great Britain affords abundant evidence that the above statement contains very much if not the whole truth, and that to no single individual is modern horticulture more indebted than to David Douglas.'

3

JOSEPH HOOKER AND HIS RHODODENDRONS 1817–1911

Joseph Dalton Hooker who was to become the most honoured British botanist of all time was born on 30 June 1817 at Halesworth in Suffolk. When only ten years old, his father boasted of him: 'My boy Joseph knows more about Botany than does Dr C.!', referring to the supposedly learned Dr Couper who coveted William Hooker's post as Regius Professor at Glasgow. When twelve years old Joseph was his father's right-hand man, helping him in his herbarium and quick to learn. It was perhaps natural that he should take to the study of plants. At Halesworth his father had been a dedicated amateur and a protégé of the great Sir Joseph Banks. By the time he was appointed to Glasgow's chair of botany he had illustrated Dawson Turner's four-volume work on Seaweeds, his paintings masterpieces of beauty and truth, and produced his own first major work – on the British Jungermanniae, a difficult tribe of liverworts. Visitors to the Halesworth house included some of the world's leading botanists. Was it any wonder that young Joseph, growing up in this scientific atmosphere and passionately devoted to his father, should take to botany as naturally as a duckling to water?

It was the ambition of every young naturalist to sail with a ship of discovery, for in the middle of the nineteenth century much of the earth's surface remained unexplored. Young men were mainly chosen who would be useful in the dual capacity of ship's doctor and zoologist. Or, because the *materia medica* of those days required a thorough knowledge of plants, young doctors were selected for their botanical knowledge. So it was with Joseph Hooker, who graduated MD just in time to sail to the Antarctic with James Clark Ross. The discoverer in 1831 of the north magnetic pole – by which the difference between the true north and the magnetic north was known, and navigators henceforward able to correct their compass readings in the Arctic regions – Ross had now been commissioned by the Admiralty to find the south magnetic pole. Joseph Hooker was twenty-two when Her Majesty's discovery ships *Erebus* and *Terror* left the Medway on 25 September 1839, the first a vessel of 378 tons, her companion of 340 tons. Both captains were experienced ice men, Ross having sailed in seven polar expeditions, with Parry, Franklin, and his uncle Sir John Ross. Captain Francis Crozier, in command of *Terror*, had also been with Parry.

Proudly, Joseph was Botanist to the Expedition. The voyage lasted four years: it was not until midnight on 4 September 1843 that *Erebus* and *Terror* were home again.

The expedition was entirely successful, and Joseph who after a chill caught in Madeira appeared to a brother officer as 'in a *very* delicate state of health ... quite unfit to undergo the fatigues of such a voyage', returned home a man toughened by danger, weathered by hard experience, and in possession of such a wealth of knowledge about plants and the wanderings of plants about the world – finding at Tierra del Fuego, for instance, the English primrose, dandelion, thrift, starwort and others – that when Charles Darwin read his introductory essay to the *Flora of Tasmania*, he exclaimed enthusiastically: 'I know I shall live to see you the first authority in Europe on that grand subject, that almost keystone of the laws of Creation, Geographical Distribution.' Joseph became Charles Darwin's closest friend, and it was to him that Darwin confided his theory of Natural Selection, a secret Hooker kept for fifteen years, until 1859 when it was published in the book that shook the established beliefs of all thinking men, *The Origin of Species*.

It is strange how the careers of the two Hookers, father and son, ran almost parallel in time. For although William Hooker did great things at Glasgow, raising the Botanic Garden there to a status equal to that of any in Europe, sending out highly trained gardeners as plant hunters (David Douglas being one), and finding posts of responsibility for his graduates in almost every corner of the globe, as early as 1836 being knighted for his services to botany, yet it was not until 1841 that he realised the dream of his life – to establish a national botanic garden. Almost as soon as he got to Glasgow he had begun planning for it. The nucleus was there, in the 9-acre royal garden at Kew which in the hands of Augusta, the Dowager Princess of Wales, and her friend the Earl of Bute, was renowned for its unrivalled collections of exotic plants. When Bute fell out of favour with Augusta's son George III, Joseph Banks, home from the voyage of the *Endeavour*, was appointed in his place. Having sailed round the world and seen the poor state of the Crown dependencies, Banks realised that the scientific study of plant life was necessary for their development. He offered his plans to the King. Kew, he said, could still be a garden where plants from every country could be enjoyed in all their beauty, but it ought to be something more, 'a great exchange-house of the Empire, where possibilities of acclimatising plants might be tested'. It was on the strength of this brilliant scheme that the King appointed him botanical and horticultural adviser to the royal garden. But before the plan could be put into action, Banks died – in 1820, just as he had succeeded in getting William Hooker appointed to Glasgow. He looked to Hooker to carry the torch for him, and this was what Hooker did, over the years enlisting the help of the influential in a period of successive governments, the outgoing one having almost come to the point of agreement, the next government having to be wooed afresh.

It was not until 1840 that, after a last bitter fight, he saw Kew – as the new Royal Botanic Gardens – become the property of the nation. In March of the following year Sir William Jackson Hooker was officially appointed its first Director.

At the other end of the world Joseph was pursuing his own career. From Madeira *Erebus* and *Terror* had sailed to St Paul's Rocks where Ross made a short series of observations, then to St Helena where he established his first magnetic observatory. It was on Napoleon's island that Joseph was confronted by a microcosmic example of the problems of geographical distribution, in the influence of imported animals and plants on the native fauna and flora. At Kerguelen's Land, which they reached after five weeks' sailing from the Cape of Good Hope, he first proved himself as a plant hunter. Captain Cook on his visit to the island had found only 18 species of plants. Joseph increased the flora to nearly 150, 18 of them being flowering plants, 3 ferns, 25 mosses, 10 jungermanniae, 1 fungus, and the rest lichens and seaweeds, and it was interesting that this vegetation was native. So remote was Kerguelen from any other land that no birds of passage came to drop seeds.

By these two experiences alone, he was already laying the foundations of his future greatness. Geographical distribution was to be his grand subject, and he was to become the discoverer of the great Sikkim rhododendrons that turned a new page in the history of horticulture.

There was a third. When the ships visited the Falkland Islands he observed the Tussac Grass. Covering tracts of poor land, it formed hillocks of matted roots from which sprang fountains of grassy foliage with blades 6ft long. Noticing the beaten paths made to the Tussac by wild horses and cattle, Joseph thought it would be useful as an economic plant providing fodder in other places where not much else would grow. He sent home seeds to his father, and after being propagated and acclimatised at Kew, the grass succeeded well in the Shetlands. Banks's idea was working.

Letters sometimes followed the exploring ships half across the world. Months would elapse before Joseph had news of his family, and news of Kew whose progress he followed eagerly as year by year its acreage expanded and its usefulness increased. One of his duties was to make collections of dried herbarium material, and Joseph saw to it that the best sets went to his father. From Tierra del Fuego he sent three Wardian cases of live young trees, writing of *Nothofagus antarctica*: 'Without seeing the deciduous beech of Fuegia no one can form an idea of the exquisite beauty of its budding leaves. I trust these trees will thrive at Kew.' There was also the beautiful Evergreen Beech (*N. forsteri*) and the aromatic-leaved *Drimys winteri*. The RHS Dictionary gives the provenance and introduction date of the first two as Chile, 1830. Loudon in his *Arboretum et Fruticetum*, 1838, does not mention *forsteri* and says of the first: 'We have never seen this tree.' Probably it did not long survive its first introduction, for the principle of the Wardian case – an hermetically sealed small greenhouse, which enabled plants to endure long journeys – had been accidentally discovered by Nathaniel Bagshaw Ward only the year before, 1829, and they were not yet in use. Lady Hooker wrote excitedly to her father, Dawson Turner: 'So valuable a consignment has not been received at the Garden (his father says) since we came here. The 2 new kinds of Beech & the Winter's Bark Tree (of the latter only one specimen was in the Kingdom before) are growing beautifully. One box weighed upwards of 3 cwt.' Before leaving Fuegia Joseph superintended the digging up of 800 young trees to be taken to the Falklands in the hope of establishing them, for timber there was scarce. Kew was much in his mind. He wrote offering suggestions. There ought to be a Pinetum, and 'Next to a good Arboretum at the Royal Gardens I should like there to be a Fern House. The noble Tree-ferns, huge *Acrosticha* and *Steganiae*, with the *Hymenophylla* creeping on the ground, would be a splendid novelty.'

Sir William could not have been better pleased at his son's interest in Kew, for he was hoping that one day Joseph might become his assistant.

Home from the Antarctic there was much to do. Besides innumerable papers for the *London Journal of Botany* on such subjects as the Antarctic lichens, a new genus of Tasmanian conifers, and a South African fossil plant, Joseph produced three monumental books: *Flora Antarctica*, in two quarto volumes, which occupied him from 1844 to 1847; *Flora Novae-Zelandiae*, 1853–5, and *Flora Tasmaniae*, 1855–60. But the writing was interrupted by the necessity of earning a living. The Admiralty put him on half-pay, which was scarcely sufficient. He applied for the Edinburgh professorship and failed to get it. Then one day Sir Henry de la Bèche came to ask Sir William Hooker to recommend an experienced botanist who could work out the British flora, living and fossil, in relation to geology. The salary was £150 with travelling allowances, and since much of the work could be done at home this would allow Joseph to continue his *Flora Antarctica*. Sir William recommended his son. He had another reason for doing so. The Geological Survey was under the aegis of the Commissioners of Woods and Forests, the same government department that ran Kew, and Sir William with his usual foresight saw that this official connection might be a way of bringing Joseph to Kew. He had need of someone to take some of the load off his shoulders – he did not even have a secretary! Expansions were going on all the time; yet still his herbarium, now the largest in private hands and used as an integral part of Kew's work, occupied thirteen rooms of his own private house. He now offered to present it to the nation on condition that Joseph was appointed his assistant and successor.

It was not to be just yet.

Joseph worked hard on the Survey, examining coal beds for fossil plants and writing three masterly essays on his findings. These received 'unstinted praise alike from geologists and from botanists'. He also completed the first part of *Flora Antarctica*. In April 1847 he was elected a Fellow of the Royal Society, of which one day he was to become president.

By then he was itching to travel again. Fossil plants were

interesting, but now he wanted to go in search of living ones.

Kew had sent out its first plant hunter in 1772, in the days of the old royal garden. This was Francis Masson who in the next quarter of a century sent back exotic plants from the Cape of Good Hope, the Canaries and the Azores, Spain, Portugal and North America. Since the death of Sir Joseph Banks it had sent out no collectors except George Barclay in 1835, though in 1843 Sir William Hooker had come to an arrangement with the Duke of Northumberland and the Earl of Derby by which the cost of sending out two collectors was shared by them and Kew. He now thought it time for another collector to be sent out. As for Joseph, he was 'ready to make any sacrifice to get to the tropics for a year', which, he was convinced, would give him the 'lift' he needed in acquiring a knowledge of exotic botany. He wrote to George Bentham (with whom he was to collaborate later on that well-known *Handbook of the British Flora*, popularly known as 'Bentham and Hooker') : 'I would not object to embark once more for a distant climate ... to explore the Islands of the South Seas, especially the Society and Sandwich groups. I might prefer the Himalaya regions ... '

De la Bèche wanted to retain Joseph on the Survey staff, and now encouraged him to go to India where he could collect fossils for the Geological Museum, the plants going to Kew. Joseph, still on half-pay from the Admiralty, was bitterly disappointed when they turned down the idea : India was out of their province. They suggested, however, that he join the expedition to the Malay Islands planned for the following year ; and by great good luck the two projects were married when, on a visit to the Isle of Man, Joseph met Lord Auckland, the 1st Lord of the Admiralty. It was now arranged that from India he should go on to join the frigate *Maeander* and prepare a botanical report on the British possessions in the Far East (though with the death of Lord Auckland in 1849 this expedition did not materialise). The way was now clear for an appeal to the Treasury for a grant of £400 a year for two years on

Kew's behalf, to cover its collector's expenses. Joseph sailed for India in November 1847, sharing his cabin with his friend Hugh Falconer who had been appointed Curator of the Botanic Garden at Calcutta.

Though collectors had visited India from the seventeenth century onwards, Sikkim in the Himalayas was entirely unexplored, and this was to be Joseph's hunting ground. He arrived at Calcutta in January, and his first expedition was a geological one with David Williams of the Geological Survey who was on the hunt for coal. They met up at Taldangah and Joseph was delighted with his mount, a clever elephant which picked up the stones he wanted and tossed them back with its trunk, 'thus saving the trouble of dismounting to geologise!' On the way westward they climbed the 4,530ft Parasnath. Joseph, never very far from his subject of geographical distribution, wanted not only to gain experience of tropical vegetation but to compare the Antarctic flora with that of the high altitudes in the tropics. Here he had his first encounter with it, the vegetation changing from tropical to temperate as he climbed higher up the mountain.

He parted from David Williams at Sulkun, and at Mirzapore he engaged a boat to carry him down the Ganges to Bhagulpore from where he was to proceed to Sikkim by palkee. Despite trouble on the way with one set of bearers who, with no relief men waiting for them, refused to carry him farther than their stage of twelve miles, which meant that Joseph had to trudge fourteen miles to the next stage, he finally arrived at Siligoree, eight miles from the base of the Himalaya.

All along the route he had been watching every change in the character of the vegetation, the plant companions of his previous excursion being replaced by ferns and then by mosses, evidence of the Himalayan influence. At Siligoree the change was sudden and dramatic. 'Every feature – botanical, geological, and zoological is new on entering this district,' he wrote in his *Himalayan Journals*, a two-volume book which is now one of the three great classics of travel. 'The change is sudden and immediate: sea and shore are hardly more conspicuously different; nor from the edge of the Terai to the limit of perpetual snow is any botanical region more clearly marked than this, which is the commencement of the Himalayan vegetation.' Gone were the stunted trees of the Terai: he climbed up to Punkabaree through a giant forest loud with the noise of mountain torrents. The deep steep gullies they had cut in the flanks of the hills were dense tropical jungle, the tumbling waters bridged by fallen trees whose trunks were richly clothed with epiphytal orchids, giant club mosses and ferns, and garlanded by such climbers as the beautiful wax-flowered hoyas.

So far, he had not seen the mountains, so thick was the tropical vapour shrouding them. He had caught a first glimpse of the outer range, sombre masses covered with dusky forest. Now as he reached Punkabaree, to the north beyond those steep hills rising 5,000 and 6,000ft around him, towered the confused masses of the Himalaya. From the travellers' bungalow he had a god's-eye view. 'The view is really superb, and very instructive,' he wrote. He saw from the hill on which he stood above the dense deep-green dripping forests, how nature had contrived such luxuriant growth. Below him to the south lay the expanse of the plains, reaching in a boundless flat to the horizon and beyond, 400 miles distant to the Indian Ocean. There the vapours were raised which formed the life-giving clouds: parallel ribbons of clouds hanging over the extreme horizon, fleecy cumuli which melted in the blue vault above the sizzling plains and re-formed as the leaden nimbi which met the mountains and discharged their burden in snow on the heights and rain below. What moisture was surplus to the forests' needs ran off in rills, rivulets and rivers coursing to the ocean where again the cycle began.

A rainy climate was to prove the key to the successful cultivation of Joseph Hooker's rhododendrons.

The first rhododendron ever to be seen in Britain, apart from the tiny Alpenrose (*Rhododendron hirsutum*) introduced by John Tradescant the younger, was *maximum*, first flowered by James

85

Gordon at his Mile End nursery in 1756. The redoubtable *ponticum* followed in 1763, commonest of all rhododendrons with its lilac heads of flowers. By 1848, before Joseph Hooker set foot in India, thirty-three rhododendrons were in cultivation, including *arboreum* of rich scarlet flowers, discovered by Captain Thomas Hardwicke of the Indian Army and introduced by Dr Nathaniel Wallich in 1827. Wallich, who was then Superintendent of the Calcutta Botanic Garden, also introduced such species as *formosum* and *campanulatum*. About the same time Dr William Griffith, the East India Company's Assistant Surgeon at Madras, discovered *grande* and *griffithianum*, though it was left to Joseph Hooker to introduce them.

Joseph far outshone them, and it is to his travels and labours that we owe our principal knowledge of the rhododendrons of the Sikkim Himalaya. His feats of endurance in obtaining them were astounding, his achievements supreme. All in the day's work of plant hunting and collecting he attained heights greater than man had yet climbed, reaching 19,300ft on Donkia, a record that eclipsed Humboldt's ascent of Chimborazo. With three peaks or passes of 18,500ft, he held the field until 1856 when the Schlagentweit brothers reached 22,230ft on Kamet. Climbing was no pastime for Joseph, for it was in the lofty heights that most of the rhododendrons had their homes, and for months at a time he did not descend below 10,000ft: this with none of the mountaineering equipment available to climbers of today.

When he left Punkabaree, Joseph was mounted on the pony sent up to him by Brian H. Hodgson, British Resident at the Court of Nepal. He set off with his bearers on a precipitous zigzag trail to reach Mahaldaram, 2,000ft higher up, and it was on the following morning that he made his first discovery, of 'a most noble Rhododendron, whose truly enormous and delicious lemon-scented blossoms strewed the ground'. He had travelled out to India with Lord Dalhousie who was taking up his appointment as the new Governor-General. In honour of Lady Dalhousie, 'I have, as a mark of grateful esteem and

86

Page 87 The magnificent Douglas Fir, named in honour of David Douglas, that man of the trees who also introduced many new flowers

Page 88 (left) The decorative
grey-green catkins of *Garrya
elliptica* named by Douglas for
Nicholas Garry of the
Hudson's Bay Company

(right) the American Flowering
Currant, one of Douglas's most
important introductions. It is
now to be found in almost every
British garden

respect, dedicated the noblest species of the whole race,' wrote Joseph of this beautiful rhododendron. In Britain it was found to be a tender subject for greenhouses. In its native land it is parasitical, always found growing on the trunks of large trees, especially oaks and magnolias. It was in an English-looking woodland where half the trees were oaks that Joseph found his treasure. Later he found another fragrant white rhododendron which was also epiphytal and could easily be confused with *dalhousiae*. When the seeds of the two were propagated at Kew, the name *lindleyi* was given to the second by Sir William Hooker in honour of his one-time protégé, John Lindley of Norfolk, who had risen to be Professor of Botany at University College, London.

The road now ran in a northerly direction along the Balasun Valley, and once across the saddle of the great Sinchul Joseph was among the mountains, the plains cut off behind him and the heights with their eternal snows ahead. Occupying a narrow ridge was the hill station of Darjeeling, his next stop, and here he met Dr Archibald Campbell who was the Superintendent there and the Governor-General's liaison officer between the British Government and the Sikkim Rajah. Campbell proved himself a friend, procuring for Joseph several Lepcha lads to act as collectors. Joseph grew fond of his Lepchas, nimble-footed cheerful little people who endured hardship with a smile, never complaining when food was scanty, stoical in a cruelly bitter climate utterly alien to them.

Four species of rhododendron grew near Darjeeling. First there was the spectacular *grande* of long leathery leaves and dense trusses of ivory-white flowers opening from pink buds. *Argenteum* was the name Joseph gave it because of the silvery-white tomentose furring the undersides of its leaves. It grew as a small tree at 8,000 and 9,000ft up, in company with laurels and magnolias, peranema ferns with fronds 2 and 3ft long, lilies of the valley and the brilliant scarlet paris of the Himalaya. Later he was to find specimens 30ft tall. Next came *campbelliae* which, in compliment to the 'amiable lady' of his new friend,

Joseph designated the rhododendron which is most charac-
teristic of the Darjeeling vegetation. It grew so thickly that
when his tent was erected the guy ropes spanned an area
between three of them. Some were a mass of scarlet blossom,
displaying, as he wrote, 'a sylvan scene of the most gorgeous
description'. *Dalhousiae*, his first treasure, which recurred here
was the third rhododendron, and Wallich's *arboreum* the fourth.

More treasures were to come, and it was on the ascent of
Tonglu on the Nepalese frontier that Joseph beheld rhododendrons in all their magnificence. At 7,000ft where the woods
were still dense and tropical with ferns, pothos, peppers and figs,
the ground was again strewn with the lily-like flowers of his
dalhousiae, dropping from the enormous oaks which were its
hosts; strewn also with the egg-like flowers of a new magnoliaceous tree, which fell before expanding and diffused a
powerful aromatic odour, strong but far less sweet than that of
the rhododendron. So conspicuous were these two blossoms
that his guides called out: 'Here are lilies and eggs, sir, growing
out of the ground!' No bad comparison, Joseph thought.
Higher up, past a region of tree ferns, walnuts and chestnuts,
they came to a new floral area where a broad-spathed arum
raised a crested head like that of the Cobra de Capel. The
paths here were much steeper and carried along narrow ridges
or over broken masses of rock which they scaled with the help of
interwoven roots of trees, and here Joseph met *Rhododendron
arboreum*, its branches hanging with mosses and lichens. Along
the flat ridges towards the top of the mountain, scattered trees
of his silver rhododendron were succeeded by *campbelliae*, and
at the very summit the tight blood-red heads of *barbatum* greeted
him, beautiful with its bright green foliage and papery light-
coloured bark. Along the north-east unexposed ridges he discovered a new rhododendron whose foliage was incomparably
the finest of all. The few branches terminated in immense
leaves, glossy green above and margined with yellow, rusty red-
brown below. The young leaves were clothed with velvety
down, the flower-heads densely crowded with small white

blossoms. One of the most striking of all rhododendrons, Joseph wrote. He thought of the friend with whom he had sailed to India, and named it *falconeri*.

The top of Sinchul was a favourite excursion for the Europeans staying at Darjeeling, to regain their health after the torrid heat of Calcutta. It was easy of access, the path to the summit passing through magnificent oak forests filled with magnolias and rhododendrons. In April and May when they were in bloom nothing could be more gorgeous. 'Not to be surpassed by anything in the tropics,' Joseph declared. Most beautiful of all was his great *argenteum* which grew here as a tree 40ft high. He marvelled again at the magnificent leaves 12–15in long, deep green, wrinkled above and silvery beneath, and the glorious masses of flowers. Again occurred his magnoliaceous shrub, which was *Michelia doltsopa*, though its introduction is generally attributed to Reginald Farrer who met it in Burma in 1919. There was a 'purple-flowered kind' which Joseph named *Magnolia campbelliae*. No authority gives an earlier introduction date than 1868 for this, the great Himalayan 'Pink Tulip Tree', yet here was Joseph finding it in 1848 as 'an immense, but very ugly, black-barked, sparingly branched tree, leafless in winter and also during the flowering season, when it puts forth from the ends of its branches great rose-purple cup-shaped flowers'. For of course in his travels in India, which lasted from January 1848 until February 1851, Joseph discovered new plants other than rhododendrons. *Magnolia campbelliae* was to prove a magnificent addition to our gardens, with its large rosy goblets opening wide to the shape of water-lilies in February and March, a well-grown tree covered with hundreds of blooms making an unforgettable sight. On Joseph's first specimen was growing his enchanting epiphytal rhododendron, *dalhousiae*.

Joseph's intention was to explore Sikkim, but his efforts to obtain permission to travel farther beyond the Darjeeling territory of Tonglo were met with stonewalled obstruction. In the autumn of 1848 Lord Dalhousie had communicated with the Sikkim Rajah, desiring him to grant Hooker honourable and safe conduct through his dominions. This was answered with uncompromising refusal. Pending new negotiations, Dr Campbell successfully applied to the Nepal Rajah for permission to visit the Tibetan passes west of Kinchinjunga, proposing in the meantime to arrange for Joseph's return through Sikkim. A guard of six Nepalese soldiers and two officers arrived at Darjeeling to conduct him to any part of the eastern districts of Nepal that he might select. Joseph decided to follow up the Tambur, a branch of the Arun river, and explore the two easternmost of the Nepalese passes into Tibet, Wallanchoon and Kanglachem, which would bring him as near as possible to the central mass and loftiest part of the eastern flank of Kinchinjunga. Horses or loaded animals of any kind were out of the question for this journey, which was to be through wholly unexplored country where sources of food were uncertain. Joseph set off with thirty porters, this time Nepalese, his entire party mustering fifty-six. Luck was with him, for after only a few days a messenger arrived with a letter from Dr Campbell announcing that the Sikkim Rajah had authorised him to return through any part of Sikkim he wished.

It was November, and at 10,385ft all annual and deciduous vegetation had long ago been passed. But soon Joseph came upon two rhododendrons, the dwarf *anthopogon* and *setosum*, both with strongly aromatic evergreen leaves. They were not in bloom: he would have to wait till next April to see *anthopogon*'s cream to deep pink flowers, and till May or June for the reddish-purple ones of *setosum*. There were no more. On reaching 13,000ft the ground was frozen; at 15,000 a path had to be cut through 3ft of snow. Only alpines grew on the summit, among them *Saussurea gossypina* which had prepared itself for a perpetual winter. Forming mounds of the softest white wool, its flowers and leaves were clothed with the warmest fur that nature could devise.

Joseph's next objective was the Wallanchoon Pass. There were daunting difficulties on the way – with provisions, with a village headman who disputed his passport, and with his Nepalese coolies who thought that long ago he would have had enough of the heights and the foul weather and they could return home. Joseph decided to send most of them back to Sikkim and press on with a picked few.

Crossing the Yangma River the road immediately climbed steeply to the south-east over a rocky moraine clad with a dense thicket of shrubs and trees. The ground was covered with the silvery flakes of birch bark and with the gossamer peelings, pale flesh-coloured and as thin as tissue paper, belonging to a rhododendron he had not seen before. He was astonished by the beauty of its leaves, bright green and 16in long. This discovery he named in honour of Brian Hodgson, the British Resident and lender of the pony, whose bungalow 800ft above Darjeeling he had shared during the rainy season, and which was to be his home again next summer. Growing 12–20ft tall and carrying dense trusses of dark magenta bells, *hodgsonii* was to prove a worthy compliment to 'my excellent friend and generous host'.

To reach the Kanglachem Valley Joseph had to cross the shoulder of Mount Nango, an hour and a half of toilsome ascent above snow beds 15,000ft up. When he saw the valley, Nango's blue ice-clad peak was only another 2,000ft above him.

The Kanglachem villagers received him kindly and provided a guide for the Choonjerma Pass which they would take for the Yalloong Valley, the most easterly in Nepal. Advised not to attempt any ascent until the next day, when they could start early, Joseph spent the afternoon botanising between the moraines near his tent where the soil was perfectly level and consisted of little lake beds strewn with gigantic boulders and covered with a hard turf of grass and sedge. The largest of the moraines was piled upwards more than 1,000ft against the south flank of the valley, and as he ascended it, climbing with difficulty, a large flock of sheep and goats overtook him on their route from Wallanchoon to Yalloong, now and again stopping to feed on the leaves of some rhododendrons. They were new.

One was the delightful shrubby *campylocarpum* of a bright cheerful green, which 'when loaded with its inflorescence of surpassing delicacy and grace, claims precedence over its more gaudy congeners, and has always been regarded by me as the most charming of the Sikkim Rhododendrons'. Thus Joseph described it, adding that the plant exhaled 'a grateful honeyed flavour' from its clear yellow bells. *Campylocarpum* is now treasured in our gardens as one of the choicest of all hardy plants. The other also became a favourite – for its attractive smooth bark, plum-coloured or cinnamon, and loose trusses of deep blood-red bells. Joseph named this magnificent species *thomsonii* for the friend who had graduated with him at Glasgow and was now Dr Thomas Thomson, surgeon with the Bengal Army. They were to plant hunt together in the eastern Himalaya, and later at Kew Thomson was to collaborate with Joseph on his massive *Flora of British India*.

After many hazardous ascents and descents, and the unpleasant discovery that he had been cheated of food supplies by the Ghorkha Havildar and his coolies (whom Joseph had nursed and clothed when they were sick and shivering among the snows), he and his party crossed the Islumbo Pass over Singalelah into Sikkim. At Lingcham news awaited him that Dr Campbell had left Darjeeling and was on his way to meet the Sikkim Rajah at Bhomsong on the Teesta River. The Rajah's prime minister had sent Joseph a pony, and thus mounted he arrived at Dr Campbell's camp, to be congratulated on accomplishing a journey which Campbell had thought almost impossible.

Back at Darjeeling, sorting out the collections he had made in the last three months, Joseph despatched them to Calcutta by coolies, carts and river boats. There were eighty loads. He now sat down to plan his next expeditions, the first to what was then believed to be the highest mountain in the world.

He left Yoksun on 7 January 1849, knowing that at this time of year he could not attain any height on Kinchinjunga but anxious to reach the lower limit of the perpetual snow. Again

94

he climbed and descended, going from deep valleys choked with tropical vegetation to mountain passes over 15,000ft amid patchy snow and glaciers. At Jongri and Chola, 10,000 and 12,000ft up he discovered *Rhododendron lanatum* growing on the rocky spurs of the humid mountain gullies. This has proved an unusual and attractive shrub, in size between a bush and a small tree. The undersides of its leaves are covered with a thick brown felt, and its bell-shaped pale yellow flowers blooming in April and May are freckled inside with crimson.

This was a good first prize for 1849.

There were other excursions while waiting for the mountain spring to bring out the flowers. He went down to Darjeeling, in February joining Brian Hodgson at Tilalya on the plains and finding a clerodendron and an osbeckia gay with blossoms like a dog rose. They went east to the Teesta river in March, and west to Siligoree. Back at Darjeeling, Joseph spent April making preparations for an expedition to the loftier parts of Sikkim. He set out on 3 May accompanied by Archibald Campbell who was going to see him across the frontier at the Great Rungeet River.

The rhododendrons were now in flower. On Tendong he saw again his lovely white-flowered *argenteum*, and then came Choongtam, a mountain some 10,000ft high dividing the Rivers Lachan and Lachoong. It was this area, which reminded Joseph of both Switzerland and the north-west Himalaya, that was to give him a rich harvest of new rhododendrons.

On the hill above Choongtam village he collected ten different kinds, of which four in the delicacy and beauty of their flowers perhaps excel any others. They were all white-flowered: *aucklandii*, *maddenii* and *edgeworthii* were all new, the fourth being his lovely *dalhousiae*. *Aucklandii* Joseph named for the 1st Lord of the Admiralty, who had been instrumental in getting him to India. This was a bush growing 4–8ft tall, whose flowers are the largest of the genus. The systematists have since named it *griffithianum*, though Joseph distinguished between the two and claimed both. *Edgeworthii*, a truly superb

95

species dedicated to 'my accomplished and excellent friend M. P. Edgeworth, Esq., of the Bengal Civil Service, now Commissioner of Mooltan', had showy sweet-scented flowers, widely bell-shaped. Its attractively peeling bark was reddish-brown, and the wrinkled surface of its leaves added much to its beauty. Joseph placed it in excellence next to *dalhousiae*. To Major Madden, also of the Bengal Civil Service and 'a good and accomplished botanist' specialising in conifers, Joseph dedicated *maddenii*. It was growing in thickets by the Lachen and Lachoong rivers at 6,000ft, another superb species, with a pale papery bark and pure white flowers tinged with a pink blush on the upper lobe. Climbing another 1,000ft up he found *salignum*, the Willow-leaved Rhododendron, a slender twiggy shrub 2–4ft tall with the scaly leaves typical of the heights. Its small trusses sometimes carried only a single flower, saucer-shaped and varying from pink to purple. *Salignum* is now better known as *lepidotum*, though again Joseph claimed the two as separate species, as he did with *obovatum* and *elaeagnoides,* though he thought that the latter might prove to be another form of *salignum*. *Obovatum* was 'a small shrub, 3–4 feet high, much branched and very resinous in odour'. Its leaves were of an opaque green above and pale yellow-brown beneath. 'The form and size of the foliage, and its glabrous upper surface, distinguish this well from *R. lepidotum*,' he stated. *Elaeagnoides* was undoubtedly the smallest species of this section, as Joseph noted. He found it growing in heather-like clumps. For its size the flowers were large, of the same form but much larger than those of *salignum* and *lepidotum*. They varied from yellow to deep red-purple. He added that this and *lepidotum* and *salignum* might prove extreme varieties of one species. As for *lepidotum*, he found this growing above 12,000ft up as a small densely tufted shrub only a foot or so tall, with flowers varying from a very fine red to a dingy yellow.

The Lachen Valley yielded him another treasure in *virgatum*, which was 'decidedly the most slender twiggy species with which I am acquainted', its branches reaching 4ft in height being scarcely the thickness of a crow-quill. Its slightly tubular flowers ran from purple through pink to white but usually were lilac-purple, and it was growing at elevations between 8,000 and 9,000ft in the fringes of pine forests in ravines. Also in the pine woods he found *candelabrum*, but this he feared was only a pale-flowered variety of *thomsonii*, though growing at a lower elevation than that species usually inhabited and flowering earlier. There were two more, both inhabitants of rocky valleys and ridges: *glaucophyllum*, a small aromatic species with bells of pale pinkish-purple rising from a circle of leaves; and the rugged-barked rhododendron he named *niveum*, which is now grown as an attractive shrub for woodlands. It can be distinguished at once by the white under-surface of its leaves. The flowers grow in tight globular heads of smoky-blue to rich purple.

From Choongtam there were two routes into Tibet, each of six days' journey. One lay to the north-west up the Lachen Valley through the Kongra Lama Pass, the other to the east up the Lachoong to the Donkia Pass. The season was at the height of the rains, and because of this the first route was pronounced impracticable, so Joseph had no choice.

There was much collecting to be done of plants other than rhododendrons. At Lamteng, three marches up the Lachen where he crossed the river, the flora was bewildering in the profusion of its variety. Conifers were of genera typical of both Europe and North America, and there were more than a dozen different deciduous trees. There were climbers and shrubs. As for herbaceous plants, these were 'far too numerous to be enumerated', wrote Joseph, 'as a list would include most of the common genera of European and North American plants'. The Japanese and Chinese floras were represented by such shrubs as camellias, hydrangeas, skimmia, enkianthus and deutzia; the Malayan flora by magnolias and orchids.

Chateng, a spur of the lofty peak of Tukcham, rose 1,000ft above the west bank of the river, and arriving at the village of Lämteng Joseph made many ascents of the mountain, hoping for a view of the snowy peaks towards the passes. Besides his botanical and other scientific equipment, he carried a sextant and an artificial horizon, and with these he calculated Tukcham's height to be 19,472ft, though this was only approximate. His calculations, however, were never far out. The height of Kinchinjunga, for instance, he gave as 28,177ft, since estimated as 28,164ft. Everywhere he went he kept careful notes, not only of the plants he found, where he found them and at what elevation, but of rocks and fossils, animals and birds. The map he made of Sikkim to illustrate his wanderings was afterwards used by the Indian Army and remained untouched until 1861. The official survey of Sikkim was not completed until 1883. It was from his botanical notes, dried specimens and coloured drawings that the great folio *The Rhododendrons of Sikkim-Himalaya* came into being. The work, edited by Sir William Hooker, came out in parts, the first of which reached Joseph in 1850 and was a wonderful reward for his labours in procuring the originals. For sometimes, as he said, it was 'like digging for daylight' to get them. (On one occasion, finding a plant on a frozen mountain-top he had to sit on it till he thawed it out.) Reviews in the newspapers were eulogies, and later Joseph told his mother: 'All India is in love with my Rhododendron book.' Publication was completed in 1851 when Joseph arrived back in England.

His problem at the moment was to find the Tibetan frontier in a country rugged and forest-clad, of tortuous and perpetually forking valleys, where paths were often obliterated and cloud and rain made the going heavy. Provisions were depleted. A large party of coolies sent from Darjeeling with rice had not arrived. While waiting for them Joseph decided to take a small party with his tent and such food as they needed, and explore the Zemu river. He made his camp on a broad terrace 10,850ft above sea level. It was sheltered by enormous blocks of gneiss and surrounded by a luxuriance of most beautiful rhododendrons in full flower, with willows, white roses, white-flowered cherry trees, thorns, maples and birch trees. Among the rhododendrons was *pumilum*, smallest of the Sikkim species, with a slender woody stem and branches only 3 or 4in long. Despite its size it had an elegant grace. The pretty pink bells of its flowers came soon after the snow melted. It occurred very rarely, in fact Joseph met it only twice in all his wanderings. Along the banks of the Zemu were dense thickets of other rhododendrons. In all, Joseph gathered thirteen different kinds in the valley, though unfortunately he does not tell us which. But we have descriptions of eight new ones collected at this time, six from the 'Interior of Sikkim-Himalaya', and two on 'Slopes and spurs'.

Of the six, *cinnabarinum* with its tubular flowers of bright cinnabar red is one of the handsomest of all Joseph's rhododendrons, looking like a fiery rocket shooting from a tail of downswept leaves. *Roylei*, similar but with nothing of such drama or such burning colour, was named in honour of John Forbes Royle, a great authority on Indian plants and at that time Professor of *materia medica* at the University of London. He recommended the introduction into India of cinchona, which Sir William Hooker later achieved. *Wallichii* was an attractive discovery with its long deep-green leaves dotted beneath with tiny powdery tufts of reddish-brown hair, and bell-shaped flowers, lilac with rose spots, up to ten in a truss. It was of course named after Dr Nathaniel Wallich. *Lancifolium* was allied to the beautiful *barbatum* but formed only a stunted shrub. *Vaccinioides* was epiphytal. Joseph found it growing on moist rocks on both the inner and outer ranges. It was a small and very slender species with bright green leaves. But it is not listed in nurserymen's catalogues and Joseph wrote: 'I have never found the flowers of this singular and very distinct little species.' Last of the six was *pendulum*, another epiphyte. It grew in the gloomy and almost impenetrable forests, and had small insignificant flowers. How different from *fulgens*, which Joseph described as 'the richest ornament of the alpine region in the month of June, pushing forth young leaves of a beautiful verdigris colour in July and August'. It was right of Joseph to

99

call attention to the beauties of a rhododendron's aftergrowth, which in some species can be as spectacular as a rhododendron's flower: bronze, silver, crimson, and through tender and unbelievable greens. *Fulgens* was one of the two he found on slopes and spurs. It quickly became a favourite with its bright scarlet trusses of bells blooming from February to April. The brilliant young shoots are, moreover, adorned with attractive crimson bracts. The other was *aeruginosum*, now named *campanulatum aeruginosum*. A slow-growing shrub of compact habit, again the young growths are striking, being a metallic blue-green. The flowers range from lilac-rose to reddish-purple. It grew at 12,400ft.

Joseph was continually being harassed and threatened by the Phipun or chief man of the village, who volunteered to show him the frontier, only to play tricks on him. And it rained incessantly. Beyond the river the skies were clearer, though all attempts to cross the river were fruitless, and the snow bridge which Joseph had hoped to use was carried away by the daily swelling torrent. But he had his rewards in botany, with two new primroses among a harvest of other plants. One was *Primula capitata*, 'a garden name embracing a whole number of allied but quite definite species, of which, to increase the confusion, several are now in cultivation'. The definition is Reginald Farrer's, and he thought the true *capitata* 'one of the miffiest and poorest of the lot'. But Joseph's primrose had a violet flower, and its leaves were slightly farinose above and snow-white farinose beneath, which seems to answer Farrer's description of *P. mooreana* with its 'stalwart white-powdered stems contrasting beautifully with the ample round head of Tyrian violet flowers'. This to Farrer was a first-class treasure and 'the one "capitata" worth having for its lavish of loveliness each year'. The other primrose was *sikkimensis*, to which Farrer gave the palm as 'one of the grandest beauties of the race with its head of hanging wide bells in the loveliest shade of soft milansoufflé yellow'.

Back at Zemu Samdong, the Singtam Soubah arrived with

orders from the Rajah (and handsome presents) to take Joseph
to the frontier. Soon after, the long-delayed party of coolies
arrived with the rice, and next day they left for the Kongra
Lama Pass and Tibet.

The path ran north-north-west and crossed the Lachen
above its junction with the Nunee. Six miles above Tungu the
river was joined by the Chomiochoo flowing from Chomiomo
mountain. The path now rose over a great ancient moraine
whose level top was covered with pools, and here, gilding the
marshes, grew his magnificent yellow cowslip, *Primula sikkimensis*. They were now above 16,000ft, and sitting down to a
meal were suddenly startled by a noise like thunder, crash
following crash and echoing through the valley. The Phipun
got up, saying coolly: 'The rocks are falling, it is time we were
off, it will rain soon.' The cliffs of Chomiomo and Kinchinjhow
were now lost in dense vapours condensing in rain and loosening
avalanches of both rocks and snow. They proceeded amidst fog
and driving rain, with, as Joseph wrote, 'the roar of falling
rocks on either hand increasing as these invisible giants spoke
to one another in voices of thunder through the clouds'. The
effect was indescribably grand, and as the weather cleared he
caught transient peeps of precipices of blue ice and black rock
towering 5,000ft above him on either side, producing a feeling
of awe that was almost overpowering. Though all around was
enveloped in gloom, there was in front a high blue arc of
cloudless sky between the beetling cliffs that formed the stern
portals of the Kongra Lama Pass.

At 17,000ft, on the loftiest bare slopes of the Tibetan frontier,
Joseph found a woody shrub spreading its small rigid branches
close to the ground. These were 'as thick as a goose-quill' and
straggled along for a foot or two, presenting brown tufts of
vegetation where not half a dozen other plants were able to
exist. Raising itself barely 2in above the soil, this was the most
alpine of all woody plants, *Rhododendron nivale*, able to withstand
the whirlwinds of the heights and endure 150 degrees of heat
when the sun beat down, and the Eau-de-Cologne perfume of

its foliage scented the air. It was rightly named the Rhododendron of the Snow. For eight months of the year it lay buried under many feet of it, and for the remaining four it was frequently snowed upon and sunned in the same hour. Through it all, it expanded its little purple flowers to the day, to be fertilised by the winds and bloom afresh.

No more rhododendrons were to be found, other plants were of little account, and at the end of September Joseph returned to Yeumtong to meet Archibald Campbell. Together they made their way back to Choongtam to follow the Lachen River up to the Kongra Lama Pass where they bluffed their way back into Tibet, spending four days in the country as they crept round the back of Kinchinjhow to the Donkia Pass, en route climbing Mount Bhomtso (18,590ft). At the beginning of the month Joseph had made his climb of Mount Donkia to the height of 19,300ft. Now he made a second attempt and again reached over 19,000ft. Though he failed to reach the summit, these climbs were no mean achievement, for mountaineering had scarcely begun even in the Alps, and it was not until sixteen years later that the Matterhorn was scaled. Yet here was a mere plant hunter attempting peaks 8,000ft higher than the Zermatt giant.

They were now going to proceed to the Chola and Yakla Passes, to get into the part of Tibet wedged between Sikkim and Bhutan.

It was on their way back to Darjeeling that Joseph and his companion were arrested on the orders of the Sikkim Rajah's prime minister. Campbell was badly treated, and the result of this final outrage in a long history of ingratitude – for the Sikkim Rajah had kept his sovereignty only under British protection – was that Sikkim was annexed by the Crown. Joseph, released after more than six weeks' captivity, spent January and February of 1850 arranging his collections and sending them down to Calcutta for shipping to England. Among them were two more rhododendrons he had discovered in the Sikkim Himalaya: *ciliatum*, a beautiful domed shrub with an attractive peeling bark and nodding rose-lilac bells; and *triflorum* of yellow funnel-shaped flowers freckled inside with green. Two others followed before he left for a trip with Dr Thomas Thomson to the Khasia mountains in Assam. These were *camelliaeflorum* of glistening leaves, whose pairs of single white flowers suggested the name; and the handsome tree-like *wightii* with its bunches of honey-scented pale yellow flowers.

Bidding farewell to India in February 1851, Joseph's home-coming in March was joyful for two reasons. Waiting for him after three and a half years' separation, was the girl to whom he was engaged, Frances, daughter of the Rev John Stevens Henslow, the Professor of Botany at Cambridge. The other excitement was to see rhododendrons already growing from the seeds he had collected. Sir William had sent sixteen pans filled with healthy young plants to Osborne for the Queen in 1850. He had sent more to his landowner friends in the West High-lands of Scotland and to others in Cornwall, Wales and Devon, districts with a mild rainy climate akin to that in their native homes. The gardens there are famous for rhododendrons, and at places like Stonefield in Argyllshire you can still see grand specimens grown from the seeds Joseph sent to Kew more than a century ago. To cite a few: an immense *cinnabarinum* 49ft tall with a spread of 25ft; *wightii* 35ft, *falconeri* the same, *hodgsonii* 40ft across and 25ft tall. Today there are few gardens and still fewer ornamental woodlands where Joseph's rhododen-drons, or hybrids from them, are not growing. Other collectors have added their rhododendrons to his: George Forrest, E. H. Wilson, Joseph Rock, Frank Kingdon Ward. But Joseph Hooker was their first great discoverer, and it was he who turned the dull Victorian shrubbery and green woodland into places glorious with colour.

Sir William's dream of having his son at Kew materialised in 1855 when Joseph was appointed Assistant Director. Ten

years later, on his father's death, he succeeded to the director-
ship to continue Sir William's great work and produce monumental floras which remain sought-after standard references.
It was at his instigation that seeds of *Hevea brasiliensis*, the best
of rubber trees, were procured from Brazil, propagated at Kew
and sent out as living plants to Ceylon and Malaya to start
the vast rubber industry. He extended the usefulness of the
Royal Botanic Gardens by adding the Jodrell Laboratory,
which put Kew into the realm of modern botanical science,
and it was there, through first experiments, that the foundations
were laid of the rayon industry.

Continually his feet itched to travel. He went to the Lebanon
in 1860, principally to study the famous Cedars; and incidentally on Darwin's behalf to study the asses, so that he could
compare their special markings with those of the zebra and
other members of the horse tribe. He visited Damascus not
long after the notorious massacre of the Christians by Syrian
Moslems. In 1871 he was in Morocco making a collection of
plants for Kew of the flora of the Great Atlas range. In 1877 he
sailed to America as Sir Joseph Hooker to explore the Rocky
Mountains. He climbed the 14,500ft high Sierra Blanca in
company with his father's old friend Asa Gray, the great
American botanist.

Charles Darwin had always relied on Joseph Hooker for
his encyclopaedic knowledge of plants, using him as a library
of information; and in December 1881, on hearing from him
how necessary was a new and complete index of all known
plants, Darwin told him that he would supply the funds. Thus
came about the *Index Kewensis*, now an integral part of Kew's
work, and one which is continuously kept up to date. It was a
wonderful climax to the friendship and collaboration of two
great men, and probably Darwin's last act for science. In
January 1882 Joseph received from him the first annual £250
to start the work that was to take ten years. In April of that
year Darwin died.

A promising young man whom Joseph had brought to Kew

Page 105 (right) Joseph Dalton Hooker as President of the Royal Society, 1873–1878. He succeeded his father as Director of Kew Gardens and became the most honoured botanist of all time

(left) His great Sikkim rhododendrons transformed dull Victorian shrubberies and woodlands into places magnificent with colour. Here is Joseph's drawing of *Rhododendron argenteum*

Page 106 (*above*) The rhododendron seeds Joseph sent home to his father at Kew were distributed to gardens with the same wet-weather climate as in the Himalaya. Now they grow happily in any garden with an acid soil; (*below*) the leaf-undersides of Joseph's *Rhododendron falconeri* are a rich rusty cinnamon. He named it for his friend Hugh Falconer, Curator of Calcutta's Botanic Garden

was William Thiselton Dyer. Fresh from the teachings of
T. H. Huxley, Dyer was of the new age, and Hooker realised
that while botany was a science of observation it must also
now be pursued as an experimental science. In November
1885 he handed over the control of Kew to the man who was
his son-in-law. (Dyer had married Harriet Hooker eight
years before.)

In 1887 Joseph received the Royal Society's highest award,
the Copley Medal, given for scientific discoveries or the ad-
vancement of science. In 1892 the Royal Society gave him the
Darwin Medal; and in 1897 on the publication of the last
volume of the *Flora of British India* the Order of the Star of
India was conferred upon him. There were other honours,
and his ninetieth birthday was a gala day, when he was given
the Order of Merit and overwhelmed with letters and decora-
tions from scientific societies all over the world. Four days
before he died at the age of ninety-four he was still hard at
work, now on balsams which he found 'terrifying' and 'deceitful
above all plants'. He named 303 new species.

There are many plants we love in our gardens that were
introduced by him, besides rhododendrons: trees – the conical
Juniperus wallichiana is his, the Himalayan birch (*Betula utilis*)
with its creamy-white bark; the exquisite (difficult but rewarding) *Myosotis hookeri* which he found as he climbed the valley
of Chomiochoo and described as 'large silky cushions ...
spangled with beautiful blue flowers and looking like turquoises
set in silver'. The handsome ornamental rhubarb *Rheum
nobile* is his, which forms pale pyramidal towers a yard high,
with transparent yellow bracts margined with pink; the musky
alpine *Delphinium glaciale* which he discovered at 16,754ft up,
and, most beautiful of all, *Meconopsis simplicifolia*, the blue
Himalayan Poppy.

So as we wander through woodland or by herbaceous
border, or stop to linger where our tiniest plants grow in our
rock gardens, we can think of him with gratitude for all the
colour and beauty he gave us.

4

PETER BARR AND HIS DAFFODILS
1826–1909

That he was nicknamed The Daffodil King tells us at once
Peter Barr's first favourite among flowers. He popularised the
daffodil at a time when it had fallen from favour. He introduced new daffodils and reintroduced 'lost' ones. Through
him, the growing of daffodils became not only a passion with
amateur gardeners but a commercial industry in many lands.

He was born on 26 April 1826 (appropriately at the height
of the daffodil season), the seventh child of a family of twelve,
at Govan on the south bank of the Clyde. Now a suburb of
Glasgow with some of Britain's largest shipbuilding yards
and engineering works, Govan was then a village of muslin
weavers. His father, James Barr, employed most of them and
was prosperous in business until he suffered a heavy loss when
a shipment of raw material on its way to him, uninsured, was
burnt on the voyage. Life became a struggle for the large family.
As soon as the boys were old enough they went out to work.
Peter was only ten when he became a draw boy to a weaver.
Quick at learning he was able after a while to do a little weaving
by himself. But it was apparent that the life of the loom was
not for him. Much more to young Peter's taste were the flowers
that grew in his father's garden, especially the tulips, of which
James Barr had a good collection. The wise father, seeing that
Peter had inherited his own love of floriculture, now allowed

him to follow his bent, finding an opening for him with James Thyne in Glasgow's Argyle Arcade. One half of Thyne's shop was devoted to the sale of seeds from his own nursery, the other half to fruit. Peter started as an errand boy but 'climbed in a short time to be the seedsman', as he told his children in the 'Brief History of the Govan Barrs' he wrote for them. Modestly he did not add that when he was put in full charge of the seed department he was not yet twenty.

Seven years of seed-selling in Glasgow gave him good experience. His next appointment was with Daly, Drysdale & Company, seed merchants of Newry, County Down, where in the fourteen months he was with them he saw the tragedies of the terrible famine caused by the failure of the potato crop. He then went to Worcester to take charge of one of Richard Smith's two seed shops. Peter Barr treasured a blue-paper catalogue issued when he was with him, and it is interesting to look through its pages. Couve Tronchuda, the Portugal Borecole, was recommended as a delicious vegetable well worth cultivating as an autumn green. The tomato was still listed under its original name of Love Apple.

A shopmate of Peter's was Tom Atkinson, an old acquaintance from Scotland, and in 1852 the two of them set up in partnership under the name and description of Atkinson & Barr, seedsmen, florists and fruiterers, at 64 High Street. One of Smith's two Worcester shops was at 61 High Street, so we can imagine the rivalry that went on, especially as the Atkinson & Barr catalogue was an almost exact replica of Richard Smith's and printed on the same blue paper. In fact there were two catalogues: 'Atkinson & Barr's Spring Catalogue of Seeds' and an 'Autumn Catalogue of Dutch Flowering Bulbs, comprising a fine collection of Hyacinths, Crocus, Narcissus, Gladiolus, Anemones, Ranunculus, Iris, Lilies, Double and Single Tulips, Amaryllis, Fritillaries, &c., &c.'

Peter Barr was in the bulb business.

Listed in the 1853 bulb catalogue were eleven different kinds of Polyanthus Narcissus, five 'Various Narcissus' including

'Bulbocodium (Hoop Petticoat)', and four Jonquils. These twenty, compared with the 128 different varieties of hyacinth offered for sale, show clearly that the daffodil was not exactly popular with the public, despite the efforts of the Rev William Herbert (later Dean of Manchester) who for years had been conducting experiments in daffodil breeding, primarily to determine which were true species and which hybrids, but work that called the attention of commercial breeders to the possibilities of the flower. In 1837 he published his book on *The Amaryllidaceae*, of which large family of some 75 genera Narcissus is one, classifying and describing about 150 varieties of daffodil.

It took some time – and the enthusiasm and labours of another man – before the daffodil idea caught on with the ordinary gardener.

Meanwhile it was soon evident to Peter Barr that he and Tom Atkinson were not going to make a success together, for his partner was bent on pleasure, he on steady hard work. He offered Atkinson the choice of taking over the business or getting out. Atkinson electing to run it by himself, Peter became manager of Wood's seed business, which kept him in Worcester for three more years, until 1859, by which time he was determined to find a larger field for his endeavours. An extra spur to ambition was that he was now married, to Martha, only daughter of the Rev George Robert Hewlings who was one of the six Clerks of Chancery before he entered the Church and became chaplain of the Countess of Huntingdon's chapel at Worcester. The family were dissenters, and this fitted in very well with Peter Barr's Scottish ideas of a no-nonsense kirk.

The larger field was London. Giving up his job with Wood's Peter made his way to Covent Garden Market, there inquiring around until he found a vacancy with the firm of Butler & McCulloch. Prospects seemed immediately rosy. He was offered a partnership, but when the contract was drawn up the terms did not accord with the verbal promises. Peter stayed on with the firm until the end of June 1861, having written a terse

letter on 1 April giving three months' notice and claiming the
£221 6s 8d arrears of salary due to him, some of it dating back
to 1859. This was a sad reproach on the firm, for, as Peter wrote
in his 'Brief History' : 'The 3rd season I was with Butler & McC.
we had the second biggest retail seed business in London.'

He lost no time in setting up his own business, later in 1861
establishing the firm of Barr & Sugden at 12 King Street,
Covent Garden, premises that were pulled down eighteen
years afterwards and rebuilt as Nos 12 and 13. The firm added
No 11 in 1900. The first catalogue, issued in September 1861,
listed a rich collection of Dutch and Cape bulbs, all fully
described and illustrated, and with advice on their cultivation.
His second catalogue appeared in January of the following
year, this time with 116 pages of interesting matter giving
descriptions and cultural notes on flower and vegetable seeds.
There is no doubt that this was the most useful catalogue of its
kind issued at that period.

The firm's nurseries were at Garratt Lane, Lower Tooting,
and there Peter Barr often arrived at 6 am to put in a couple of
hours or so before a hurried breakfast, then away to his shop
in Covent Garden where he usually stayed late: he thought
nothing of working twelve or fourteen hours a day. His particular interest at the nurseries was the study of various families of
plants whose nomenclature required putting in order. These
included irises, peonies, hellebores and lilies, of which he had
built up wonderful collections. Indeed, his lily collection was
the largest and finest in existence at the time, and he spent
years in classifying them, popularising them through his elabo-
rate catalogues, later ones being illustrated with drawings and
paintings by his daughter Agnes. His labours greatly facilitated
J. G. Baker's work for his *Handbook of Amaryllidaceae* and that of
J. H. Elwes in writing his magnificent monograph of *The Genus
Lilium*. Elwes showed his appreciation by presenting him with
an autograph copy.

On his father's death Peter had sold his tulips – and thought
no more about them until a Dutch amateur came to him asking

if he could dispose of his collection of tulip bulbs which nobody wanted to buy. Peter thought back to the Govan days when his father's garden there had glowed with tulips, and his interest was reawakened. He started to investigate and found that the English and especially the Lancashire growers worked from a different standard than that of the Dutch. He went up to Scotland in search of tulips, and found only one named collection, at Falkirk. But in other places he picked up a good many, chiefly in Dunfermline. Then after procuring all he could from Holland, he turned his attention to England, to find that Charles Turner, the famous nurseryman of Slough, had given up cultivating them. A Mr Goldham of Mitcham had been the owner of a unique collection, but Peter Barr could trace neither him nor his bulbs until a lady in Essex asked him to call and see her tulips. He bought them at 10s per 100 and discovered to his joy that they were all that remained of Goldham's collection. He went on collecting tulips, in the Midlands and elsewhere, and the result of his comparative trials showed that the Midland growers had the finest types of florists' tulips. The practical outcome was that Peter Barr made tulips fashionable, not the fancy varieties of Bizarres, Flames and Feathers but the lovely 'breeders', and a few of the finest of the species tulips.

But of all plants, daffodils came first in his affections. He set to work to collect together every species and form known in Britain and Europe. His correspondence, both home and foreign, became voluminous as he begged or bought from raisers, garden-owners and botanic gardens. Wishing to know what 'Narcissus Scoticus' was, he wrote sixty letters to likely people in Scotland, asking for bulbs, and was successful in obtaining a few clumps. Alongside these he cultivated the English form and discovered that the latter and the French were the same, and the Scottish and Dutch identical. Arising out of this, he once put the profound query: 'Are the Scots Dutch, and the English French?' He read old herbals such as John Parkinson's *Paradisus*, published in 1629, and listed daffodils no longer in cultivation. Astonished to discover that in Parkinson's time as many as ninety-four varieties were being grown in England, he decided that one day he would explore their native homes in the Pyrenees, Spain and Portugal, find them and restore them to English gardens.

Dean Herbert had inspired two men in particular to hybridise daffodils. One was Edward Leeds, a stockbroker of Longford Bridge, Stretford, Manchester, who owned a fine old garden near the River Mersey and spent all his leisure time in it, growing old florists' flowers such as auriculas, carnations, pinks and tulips, and raising daffodils, concentrating on improving the white and pale-coloured varieties. In 1874, being in poor health and crippled, he decided to dispose of his whole collection of daffodil seedlings consisting of 169 different varieties. No buyer came forward, and bitterly disappointed he made a will that in the event of their not being sold his bulbs and all his papers were to be burnt. On hearing of this, Peter Barr wrote to Leeds to inquire what sum he was asking, and was told that it was £100. This was more than he felt he could afford, but anxious that the valuable collection should not be lost he formed a small syndicate. The bulbs, numbering 24,223, with small ones which had not yet bloomed, were divided among the five partners in the venture: five-tenths to Peter Barr, three-tenths equally between the Rev John Gudgeon Nelson of Aldborough Rectory, Norfolk, a relative of the great admiral, W. Burnley Hume and his brother-in-law Herbert J. Adams, an entomologist of Enfield, and G. J. Brackenridge, the balance of two-tenths being taken by Peter van Velsen of Overveen, the only Dutch nurseryman who had thought it worth while to subscribe!

In succession to Leeds as a daffodil hybridist came William Backhouse of St John's, Wolsingham, County Durham, who began making crosses in 1856. A banker by profession, he squeezed in time to do his hybridising in the morning before leaving to catch his train for the office. His laboratory, so to speak, was a small glass porch leading out of his study, the daffodils intended for hybridising being grown in pots. Backhouse aimed at getting better-coloured flowers, his first favourites being the red-cup varieties. The well-known trumpets Emperor, Empress and Weardale Perfection were all of his raising, and still in demand is his W. P. Milner (named after his brother-in-law), a little pale-coloured bicolour trumpet which sells in thousands every year for planting in rock gardens.

William Backhouse predeceased Edward Leeds, and in 1869, several years after Backhouse's death, Peter Barr bought his collection of seedlings. It took time to sort them out, for no record could be found of his various crosses, and so Barr could only speculate as to how they had been made. Also, some of the seedlings had been mixed. But eventually the collection was found to contain 192 distinct sorts; so that with the 169 Leeds seedlings Peter Barr found himself the proud possessor of 361 distinct new daffodils.

It was interesting to compare the two collections. In Peter Barr's own words, when later he told the story to Luther Burbank, the great American hybridiser whom he inspired to grow daffodils, William Backhouse had been 'a rather large, coarse, strong, dominating type of man – not a repulsive man by any means, but lacking, a little, in refinement and the more delicate sensibilities', and his daffodils were the bright bold red-cup ones; while Edward Leeds, 'a highly sensitive, nervous, shrinking man with a great eye for detail, a true appreciation of values, a man who looked beneath the surface of things and saw beauty in hidden truths, a man who thought much and said little' had bred daffodils that were 'charmingly delicate – not hardy but rather shrinkingly artistic – not loud in their colour schemes but softly alluring with their subdued hues'.

Peter Barr now enlisted the help of John Gilbert Baker, Keeper of Kew's Herbarium, in evolving a classification into which the various new forms could be placed for easy identification. From a botanical point of view the grouping adopted was an artificial one, but it did afford a convenient system for future hybridists. Peter Barr had always been given generous help from Frederick William Burbidge, Curator of Trinity College Botanical Garden, Dublin, and an ardent daffodil lover, and when the names were chosen for the different subdivisions one was Burbidgei, with Leedsii, Humei, Backhousei, Nelsonii and Barrii. Thus were the six commemorated who had done so much to further the cause of the daffodil and save two priceless collections from extinction. In 1882, on the death of John Gudgeon Nelson, Peter Barr acquired his collection. It comprised all the old forms known to amateur horticulturists from the seventeenth century, together with Nelson's portion of Leeds's seedlings and a few new and distinct seedlings he had raised himself.

The next two years were triumphant ones for Peter Barr. In 1883 the partnership of Barr & Sugden was dissolved and the business became Barr & Son. In 1884 the seal of recognition was set upon the daffodil. For with the advent of so many hybrid daffodils and with a system of classification that called for official ratification, Peter Barr, J. G. Baker and F. W. Burbidge decided to ask the Royal Horticultural Society to hold a special conference. It took place on 1 April 1884. Peter Barr on acquiring the Leeds and Backhouse collections had classified the varieties according to their parentage and structural characters. This was the form of classification he had taken to J. G. Baker, and now at the conference it was discussed and in the main accepted. The conference also gave great stimulus to the Royal Horticultural Society itself, for a resolution was adopted that 'garden varieties of Narcissi, whether known hybrids or natural seedlings, should be named or numbered in the manner adopted by Florists, and not in the manner adopted by Botanists'. To carry the resolution into effect the Narcissus Committee was formed under the wing of the Scientific Committee, two years later to be empowered with the recommending of First Class Certificates and Awards of Merit, and finally to function independently.

Now an extension of the conference catalogue was called for, and it fell to the expertise of Peter Barr to compile it. His Supplementary Catalogue, published in the June, July and August 1884 issues of *The Florist and Pomologist*, reads like a star cast of celebrities of the day: the famous singers Jenny Lind and Sims Reeves were there, Grace Darling, Sir R. Peel, Chinese Gordon, Charles Dickens, Sir Walter Scott, John Bright, Joseph Chamberlain and Gladstone, with royal families well represented in Prince Teck, Her Majesty of course, the King of the Netherlands, Princess Mary (one of the most famous daffodils of all time), and Lords and Ladies galore. There were leaders of the horticultural world such as Maurice Vilmorin of the famous Paris seed firm, William Robinson, the great plantsman and pioneer of herbaceous borders, Gertrude Jekyll, and Katharine Spurrell whose collection of daffodils eventually went to the RHS garden at Wisley. The Barr family featured Agnes Barr, Alice Barr and Ellen Barr, Peter's three daughters, and P. R. Barr, J. W. H. Barr and George H. Barr, his three sons. There was no Martha: Peter's wife had died in the 1870s. But there was Aunt Jane, for Peter's sister, a beloved member of the family.

Later in 1884 Peter Barr published – and his friend F. W. Burbidge illustrated with wood engravings – *Ye Narcissus or Daffodyl Flowre, and hys Roots with hys Historie and Culture*, a rather fanciful title for a volume packed with interesting and useful information, but by this time Barr was steeped in the language of the old herbals. Burbidge, an authority on the history of the daffodil, wrote on the myths and poetry connected with the flower, its geographical distribution, its structure and botany; and Peter Barr gave the 'Compleat Liste of all the Species and Varieties known to Englyshe Amateurs'. This was the Descriptive Supplementary Daffodil Catalogue he had compiled for the Royal Horticultural Society. It included all the daffodils known to L'Obel, Clusius, Turner, Gerard and Parkinson, as well as those of Haworth and Herbert, Baker, Burbidge and Peter Barr himself. Not all of them having

been identified with living plants, these were marked in the list
by an asterisk and were the ones Peter Barr set off to find in
1887.

His sons had inherited his love of plants, particularly bulbous plants, and Peter Rudolph, the eldest, was now of an age
to run the business in his absence. He was twenty-five when his
father left England to find the 'lost' daffodils.

Living at Oporto, where he had been born, was the botanist
Alfred Wilby Tait, who was also the Baron de Sontellinho.
Tait was interested in the daffodils growing around Oporto and
in other parts of Portugal, and had been corresponding about
them with other daffodil lovers including Peter Barr and the
Rev C. Wolley-Dod, a retired schoolmaster living at Chester
and a great gardener. He was generous in sending them bulbs,
among them varieties of *Narcissus triandrus*, the miniature
daffodil with three hanging cups. But two others had really
aroused Barr's interest. One was *N. johnstonii* which Tait had discovered in 1886 (it was to win an RHS First Class Certificate
in 1887) and named after his friend Ernest Johnston, discoverer
of the other daffodil which interested Peter Barr, the quaint
little *cyclamineus*. This, figured by Olaf Rudbeck, the seventeenth-century Swedish botanist, had been lost to cultivation for
over 200 years. Indeed, Dean Herbert declared it 'an absurdity
which will never be found to exist!' Peter Barr was now fired to
delay no longer in taking up Tait's invitation to come out and
see what else might be found.

He left London in February and travelled via Bordeaux,
Bayonne and San Sebastian, and on through the Cantabrian
Mountains. It was on this Spanish journey that he tried to book
a single room at an inn, and on being informed by the landlord
that only a double-bedded room was available, for which he
would have to pay accordingly, Peter Barr, a Scot who liked
getting his money's-worth, spent half the night in one bed and
half in the other. At Oporto he lost no time in going on a first

foray, when Alfred Tait took him four miles out of the town to the church of Matlosinhos. Behind the church was heathland with fine old pine trees, and here grew an abundance of *Narcissus triandrus albus*. Tait had sent him bulbs of these, which Barr & Son had exhibited in flower at the Daffodil Conference. Mixed with them was the dwarf yellow Ajax (*N. minor* var. *nanus*) which Dean Herbert had grown. 'A higher development of N. minor, crown 6-lobed,' Peter Barr noted in his diary.

Each day brought something of interest. At Pont de Pereiro he saw *johnstonii*, sometimes with two stems, each having two flowers. *Cyclamineus* was growing in little colonies on the headlands of fields, 'as if they had been thrown up when the soil was being cultivated'. Very often Ajax was growing among gorse, and Mr Tait told him that the potash contained in the gorse maintained the fertility of the land in Portugal, concluding that 'Without the rotation of crops, seeing that Narcissus Ajax grows with the gorse, potash must be the food it uses.'

It was a bad day when he reported: 'Found nothing.' Sometimes he went by coach or carriage, other times on horseback, and always accompanied by José-Maria, a Portuguese lad recommended to him by Alfred Tait. Together they scaled the mountains, climbing 3,500ft up the Serra de Gerez range and discovering a small yellow *Narcissus corbularia* with erect foliage. José-Maria was useful as a plant hunter. He 'found in an orchard a yellow Narc. Ajax with perianth slightly lighter in colour than the trumpet, trumpet full with very thick tube, differing in this respect from the yellow maximus'. The narcissus was reported to be found wild in the mountains. 'José Maria to make a special journey to get more, and also of some at Povoa de Lanhozo,' Peter Barr was pleased to note. A large yellow Ajax was found by a woman at the general store where they baited their horses at Gerez.

At Ovar, where he explored in the middle of March, he noted the variations occurring among the *corbularia* or Hoop Petticoat Daffodils.

In the meadows in close damp soil, the large yellow Narc. corbularia grows abundantly, some of them 1ft high with foliage lying on the ground. In pine woods close by grows a small fine-leaved Narc. corbularia, in sand or sandy loam. In some places flowers are very open. In some the petals stand out at right angles, in others they are close up against the corona, as in Parkinson's plate. The flowers vary in size and form and some are quite small. All, however, have the very thin fine foliage, quite distinct from those in the meadow which have large foliage and bulbs. The Narc. corbularia growing near the railway station have among them many of an orange colour, very fine, growing in sand or sandy loam, the richest-coloured ones being among young pines.

From Frone to the River Crestuma where they were on 25 March no daffodils were to be found, although they traversed eight miles of its course. There were other plants, however: two species of polygala, one a Tyrian purple of compact growth, the other 'pale carmine-blue', as Peter Barr described it, and of straggling habit. *Pinguicula lusitanica* was growing on clayey slate rock in constant moisture, and the honey-scented *Cheiranthus hispanicus* in chinks of the rocks fully exposed to the heat of the sun. Next day they drove to Carvalho and from there to the upper waters of the Avinles River where, growing on the banks, they found *Narcissus cyclamineus* in seed. Descending the river to Ponte de Pereiro they collected *johnstonii*.

They were close to the Spanish border, and Peter Barr was making Spain his next hunting ground. It was now nearly the end of March. He and José-Maria left Oporto for Orense and reached Valença de Minho in the afternoon. At Tuy their luggage was examined by the customs. After a wait of three hours at Guillarey they finally boarded a train for Orense 'which we reached about 10 p.m., but the noise in the house was so great could not get any sleep until after 12 o'clock. When the men and women had gone to bed, two cats commenced the fun and kept it up well through the night'. However, Peter was up at 6.30 and after breakfast set out for the botanic gardens where he saw *Narcissus johnstonii*, *N.*

incomparabilis plenus, two forms of *N. tazetta*, *N. intermedius major*, *N. odorus*, and *N. ajax* which was out of bloom. Disappointingly there was nothing new, and although they walked all day rewards were few: *triandrus* with a clear yellow tube, and a white *triandrus*. José-Maria helped him collect the plants and wrap them up in damp moss and calico.

With Orense as their base they went out each day in a different direction, and on 2 April were following the Rio los Ponjos when they found a large clump of an Ajax Narcissus, 'either Bicolor or Johnsoni, which we at once bagged and made vigorous search for more'. This was a new discovery, which Peter Barr later named Queen of Spain. He described the roots as growing 9in deep in a strong yellow loam, in an oak wood 'which would give shade in summer'. How careful he always was to note down the kind of soil and situation where he found his daffodils, so that he might pass on the information to his nursery and to his customers. And to help other daffodil seekers he meticulously gave their provenance. Thus on the following day:

> At Santa Maria Reza, on the banks of the Minho, a short distance from Orense on left bank of river, in meadows on both sides of the road, found Narc Ajax in quantity. They had finished flowering, but appeared to be the same as the Oporto var. The largest quantity were to be found on the left side of the road and at the top of the bank which in summer would be the driest position.

They were not the same as the Oporto var., a Tait discovery which he was already growing under the name Oporto Yellow, but another new daffodil, and this he named Santa Maria. It had a small deep-golden trumpet and twisted petals, and with the Queen of Spain it proved to be one of the two best miniature daffodils for our rock gardens.

The Spanish spring was beginning to go over. But on 8 April on the road to À Verin, some miles past a place called Villa Nova, they came to the River Calvas, and growing on its brink and spreading along for 200–300yd was a yellow Ajax. They were all out of bloom except one faded flower. He collected a basketful of bulbs, noting in his diary: 'Similar to the Portuguese var.' But again it was something new. Later he named it Calvas Yellow.

Peter Barr spoke no other language than English, and that in a thick Glasgow accent which his grandchildren found almost incomprehensible. In order to locate the daffodils he was looking for he carried about with him paintings of them and arriving at a likely place he would show them to the local peasants. At Tundias, farther along the À Verin road, he displayed a picture of the yellow Ajax, anxious to get a good haul of them. A villager immediately offered to take him on Sunday to where they grew. On his return to Orense in the evening it was to find that José, all on his own, had collected a second basket of the Ajax, so that their haul for the day was nearly 2,000 bulbs. The Sunday excursion to Allarez, whither they were led by their peasant guide, was even more rewarding. The daffodils were growing in tens of thousands. No wonder that his entry for 12 April was: 'Packed bulbs for London.' Boxes 1 and 2 contained about 2,500 bulbs from Santa Maria and Reza, Boxes 3 and 4 about 1,600 Ajax from the River Calvas, with 700 from Allarez and 300 from Venta de Solo-Penedo.

23 April found the two at Oviedo on the Cerdino River. Close to the town on a north-facing bank, Peter discovered a new daffodil which he named Pandora No 2. He collected 100 large bulbs, 430 flowering roots and 220 small bulbs. On the same day he collected 1,400 bulbs of another new daffodil, growing on the sloping banks of the River Nora. Again they were out of bloom, except one damaged bulb flowering late. 'Flower white or pale sulphur. Call this Spanish White of Northern Spain,' Barr wrote in his diary. He indexed it as 'No. 4 Ajax'. Another discovery was *Narcissus asturicus flore pleno*, the double form of Parkinson's 'Early Strawe-coloured Bastard Daffodil' which W. d'Arcy G. Osborne had sent him in 1882. At Tooting two years later it had flowered for the first time in England for nearly 300 years.

The Oviedo expedition yielded a tremendous haul of thousands of bulbs: *Narcissus triandrus albus*, a large sulphur Corbularia daffodil, Ajaxes and Romuleas, with scillas and 900 corms of *Crocus asturicus*. The task of digging them up was sometimes made easier by enlisting the help of local boys, especially when some bulbs had to be 'got out of the marshy black soil'. Many of the daffodils grew near streams and wet feet were the order of the day. It was unfortunate that, thinking to help, 'At the Hotel, they baked my shoes in the oven and destroyed them.' Peter had to proceed in a pair of wooden ones.

They were at Vigo on 12 May, lodging with Signora Diez and being waited on by her daughters Aurora and Felicia. It was a cheerful household, if spartan, the mattresses of the beds being of Indian corn leaves. Peter was on the hunt for *Narcissus cyclamineus*. Tait had sent him some bulbs in 1886, which he flowered in time for the RHS show on 8 February 1887, winning Barr & Son a First Class Certificate. Now he was anxious to collect a quantity for his nurseries, and when he showed the Diez girls a painting of it they recognised it immediately, and directed him to a brook near the house where they were abundant. This exquisite little daffodil is now one of the treasures of our gardens, delighting in damp spots and shady nooks in the rock garden and naturalising itself in grass. Peter always found it growing in the wettest of places, its bulbs even in water. At Pontevedra, he found the polyanthus daffodil which he sent home under the name *Tazetta virginea*, suggested by its pure white perianth.

On 23 May he and José-Maria returned to Oporto where the handsome *Iris boissieri* of red-purple standards and blue falls was in full bloom in Alfred Tait's garden. The Rev Charles Wolley-Dod had supplied Peter Barr with a list of places in France where he should look for daffodils, and on 28 May the sturdy little Scot bade Mr Tait a hearty farewell and set out to follow the spring north across the Pyrenees. 1 June found him at Bayonne where a short way down the river in pine woods he

Page 123 Peter Barr was called The Daffodil King. He reintroduced 'lost' daffodils, introduced new ones and started daffodil-growing as an industry in many lands

Page 124 The two tiny daffodils *Narcissus cyclamineus* (*above*) and *N. triandrus albus* (Angel's Tears) (*below left*), with the great white daffodil Peter Barr (*below right*), bred at his nurseries

found *Muscari plumosum* growing among a mass of white cistus. There was no trace of a daffodil: he was too late for *Narcissus pallidus praecox* and for the others Wolley-Dod had listed. Moving on to St Mégard in the Basses Pyrénées he met M Dubroca Aubergest. 'A decent looking man,' Peter commented. 'I showed him my pictures and he at once picked out Maximus as the one known at Orthez as Fleur Curé,' adding: 'I made this known to Madame Planteau and asked her to write or go over to see.' Orthez was a station no great distance along the line from Bayonne, but Peter Barr does not seem to have had any results from this. He went on to Luz via Pau and Lourdes, and on being told that narcissi were everywhere in the meadows, 'went out with maid servant in search but found none. Consulted other parties with same result.'

He went in search of a professional guide. These were the men who knew not only every slope and crag of the mountains but the flowers that grew on them. All were away from home, two having gone to the Val d'Arras after white narcissi (news which set Barr's ears tingling), but another would return that night. He left a message for him to call at his hotel for a chat about his route (which now, of course, would take in the Val d'Arras.) A horse would be necessary, a donkey or a mule, and as it was customary here (different from Spain) to ride with a leather saddle Peter thought he had better have a lesson in keeping his seat. It was not very successful, for 'my feet were in a line with the horse's head, and my back hove against an upright'. However, next day, 16 June, he set off at 5 am on horseback, Henri Passet, his guide, riding a mule. 'Remained on its back as far as it could go,' Peter Barr wrote. 'When the horse was done up, Passet and I started on foot over the snow and reached the ridge of the mountain.' They were in the midst of the Pyrenees in the country bordering France and Spain, their route ahead roughly a semicircle reaching to Luchon. It was Barr's intention to search each col and valley on the way, with first a foray to Mount Perdu across the frontier.

Coming down the mountain, enjoying the splendid view of

valleys and peaks, they were challenged by soldiers looking for a notorious Spanish brigand called Zorilla and suspecting that Barr was their man. Their commandant knew he was not and courteously invited them to lunch, after which they proceeded along a rough bridle-path. Peter, this time on the mule, was astonished how the animal ascended the sharp inclines and crossed rivers knee-deep among large boulders. By late afternoon they were in the Val d'Arras, among mountains grander and wilder than anything he had yet seen. 'The formations remind me of cathedrals and castles of crystal,' he wrote. They slept that night under a ledge of rock and were up again at 4 am to begin their ascent to the white narcissus.

It was a long and arduous trudge, and when they reached the top it was to find the ground cleared and two members of Henri Passet's family, Celestin and Pierre, in charge of a mountain of 12,000 bulbs they had been commissioned to collect. Very few remained undug, and these also were to be added to the pile. 'Went in search of other habitats,' was Peter's philosophic ending to that story.

He found them. At the base of Mount Perdu they came upon the same white narcissus – and other white ones, some with trumpets as large as *cernuus* and *tortuosus*, some with blooms uniformly small. At 7,000ft up he came on the small one again. It was Parkinson's miniature white daffodil, *Narcissus moschatus*, lost to cultivation since 1629. That night they camped under another rock ledge, but this time on mattresses of green leaves, and after supper they celebrated by singing Spanish songs till bedtime. Next day the Pic de Poujaston rewarded him with a new narcissus whose petals were of the palest yellow. He called it Blanc Doré.

Luchon greeted them with rain, thunder and lightning, and as soon as the worst of the storm was over they made for their hunting ground, the Pic de l'Entécade where between 5,000 and 6,000ft up they collected the beautiful *Narcissus bernardii*, ranging in colour from yellow- to orange-stained cups. It was growing among *nobilis*, which was plentiful, and *poeticus* which was not so plentiful. Two people had collected it before him: in 1878 the Hon Mrs Barton of County Kildare, in 1881 H. E. Buxton. But now it went into commerce, as did *Narcissus abscissus*, another Parkinson daffodil and the parent of the modern Will Scarlet which caused a sensation when it was first shown by the Rev G. H. Engleheart. Its twisted perianth was rated 'disgraceful' by the connoisseurs. But nobody could ignore the brilliance of its fiery orange-red crown.

There were climbs to other peaks, long marches to hunting grounds, one of eight hours. Sometimes 'we searched in vain for Narcissi'; other times the harvest was rewarding. On the Col d'Espingo they found a form of *variiformis* with a sulphur-white perianth and a yellow trumpet; *muticus* in the Val d'Esquierry, and *poeticus*. They were growing on steep slopes among seas of asphodels and gentians.

Luchon was Peter Barr's last hunting ground that year. On 7 July he left for St Jean de Luz, Bayonne and England, arriving home on the morning of the 18th, having been absent for five months.

Spain and the Pyrenees called him again in 1888, and this time he worked his way down the coast from Arcachon to Corunna, and inland across to Vigo, returning through Galicia and Asturias, to finish as before in the Pyrenees. Again Henri Passet was his companion, but although the season was earlier – he left London in February and arrived to find France under snow – he discovered only three new hybrids in six weeks. There were, however, plenty of the Corbularia type of daffodil, especially *citrina*, also *pallidus praecox*. 'Large quantities,' he wrote, and certainly the numbers he shipped home make hair-raising reading: 'About 7,000 bulbs ... About 6,000 bulbs ... ' and on one occasion, 'Small yellow Corbularia, 11,800.'

His visit to San Sebastián 'was of more than usual interest. I met quite a nice lot of people and we all chummed up and

were very jolly.' Among them were a Mrs Hossack of Muizen-
burg, Cape Town, and 'a very amiable young lady' who was
the Comtesse Mathilde Wahuys, her full name being Mathilde
Wilhelmine Alexandrina Anna Chretienne, as Peter Barr noted
with interest. Mrs Hossack invited him to visit her in South
Africa. Indeed, the widowed Peter Barr seems to have had an
eye for the ladies, and at Santander, finding 'an Eryngium-
looking plant' he 'Sent to Miss Jekyll' who was to become
famous as a gardener and writer on gardening. Quite a romance
developed between them. From Santander, en route for Asturias,
he lost all trace of daffodils, finding them again along the banks
of the Scilla, though in small quantities, and again losing them
at Rivadesilla. A meadow not far from Oviedo yielded *pallidus
praecox* and *corbularia citrina* growing together, but there was no
sign of any hybrids. Farther on, near the village of Corredoria
pallidus praecox was abundant along the banks of the Nora, and
by a tributary of the Gafo he came upon his first hybrid, in
hue resembling *johnstonii* but more lemon-coloured.

At Verina he found a curious *triandrus albus*, of which
twenty-one flowers had the pistil protruding and eleven did
not; and on the road out of Aviles he found a hybrid of *pallidus
praecox* and *triandrus*. It is difficult to trace these hybrids, for
Peter Barr described them in his diaries only sketchily and
pressed no specimens for identification – though this was
sometimes impossible, as when he collected out-of-flower bulbs,
relying on a peasant's word that they were something different.
Often, therefore, he had to wait to see what came up in his
nursery. One happy surprise greeted him after the 1887 trip,
for instance, when in the following spring a new little daffodil
made its appearance. This was his Queen of Spain, a natural
hybrid of *triandrus albus* and the wild Spanish trumpet daffodil,
12in high with a trumpet of a delicate canary-yellow.

The charming little yellow *cyclamineus* daffodil had become
an instant favourite, and now on the Vigo road by Pondella
and at Saleedo it was plentiful. Between them Peter Barr,
Henri Passet and two boys collected nearly 3,000 bulbs. Peter

added a *tazetta*, a *pseudo-narcissus*, a trumpet daffodil, Parkinson's small yellow Hoop Petticoat, and the true *minimus* of Parkinson, smallest of all the trumpet daffodils, only 3in tall, which was known but was not generally in commerce. Several new peonies also went back to his nurseries. The most important was 'a wooly leaved plant not in flower but with bud. (? sp.)'. The species was the beautiful rosy-flowered *coriacea*.

Not having sufficient room in his Tooting nurseries to accommodate so much new stock, Peter Barr had previously sent portions of the Leeds and Backhouse collections to be grown for him by Simon de Graaff at Leiden, and from these several fine trumpet hybrids were raised, the best being the now well-known Madame de Graaff. This, the first of the larger white trumpets, had received a First Class Certificate the year before. Peter returned home in June to find it fetching £5 a bulb, one of the first high prices to be asked for a daffodil.

In 1889 he moved his nursery to larger space at Surbiton, and did not go abroad that year as he was too busy superintending replanting. In the following year he explored Brittany and the sea-swept Glénan Islands, finding *Narcissus triandrus calathinus*, one of the most beautiful little daffodils in existence, on the Île Drenec where, alas, it no longer grows, the sea having washed away its home. He was absent from the Second Great Daffodil Conference and Exhibition, held at the Royal Horticultural Society's garden at Chiswick from 15 to 18 April, when Barr & Son were awarded a Gold Medal for their exhibit.

In 1891 he did much plant hunting by proxy, carrying on a detailed correspondence with Robert N. Nancarrow, a Cornishman who lived at Ribadavia in the Orense province, and with Juan Mesa of Corunna, both of whom had helped him on previous visits to Spain. The actual collector was a Spanish lad by the name of Angel. Nancarrow was a mines inspector, and he and his wife ran a Sunday school for Spanish children. Angel Gancedo was one of their pupils. In 1892 Angel was to become Barr's factotum, hiring transport, acting as interpreter, beating down prices and, most importantly, collecting daffodils. 'My

boy Angel,' Peter Barr called him affectionately – and sometimes ironically, for Angel, though well trained by Nancarrow
in daffodil-spotting, could be exasperating. On his second
expedition for Barr he found a new narcissus at Celanova, about
fifteen miles south of Ribadavia: it was *intermedius*, of small
flowers with a deep orange cup. On the other hand he had a
mañana habit of saying 'Next year ... ', causing Nancarrow to
complain: 'He tries the bit of patience I have very often.'
Again, he faithfully despatched sacks of thousands of bulbs, but
kept missing certain daffodils Peter Barr wanted, when he
would return so humbly apologetic that Nancarrow was moved
to write: 'Poor fellow, poor fellow ... he is quite crestfallen.'

In 1892 Barr decided to hunt again in person. He left
London for Gibraltar on 25 February in the P&O ship
SS *Carthage*, and after a short sight-seeing tour he travelled
through the Algarve to Coimbra where he met his friends the
Taits, spending a few days with them at Oporto. He went on
to Corunna, on the way picking up Angel at Ribadavia.

The first hunting grounds were in the Corunna district and
south to Santiago de Compostela, then along the coast to
Cambados and Pontevedra, inland to Celanova and Palencia,
and on to Avila which they reached on 11 May. The following
day they set off by train for El Escorial, peering out of the
carriage windows to see what might be found. Angel spotted
Narcissus corbularia in abundance on the left, Barr seeing the
same from his window. El Escorial was obviously going to be
rewarding.

It was. They found the meadows full of *Narcissus graellsii*,
another dainty Hoop Petticoat, with *pallidulus* nearby, and
rupicola on the steep hillside opposite, a rock-loving miniature
daffodil with rush-like leaves and a cup-shaped orange-yellow
corona. They collected frantically for the next two days, on
16 May travelling by coach to La Granja. Now they were in
the heart of the Sierra de Guadarrama where, a century BC,
the Romans quarried huge granite rocks for Spain's largest
aqueduct. La Granja was an interesting old town with its

college church and Palace of San Il Defonso, though Peter Barr
thought much more could have been made of its gardens. The
following day he and Angel went to the mountains of Penalara,
at 1,500ft up finding *Narcissus rupicola* growing among the rocks.
It was not abundant, but they managed to scratch up about
2,000 bulbs. Another 500ft up they found it again, close to
Crocus carpetanus growing in sheets of delicate lilac. On the
following day they went to the mountains of Mata Duezes 'and
there collected a form of *N. graellsii* but more sulphury in
colour, some almost white, still not like the one at the Escorial'.
They were Hoop Petticoat daffodils but among them were
some *triandrus albus*, of which Peter could never have enough.
'So I sent Angel back to collect some more.' Spain was very hot.
Up in the granite mountains it was sizzling. The work of prising
out the bulbs from the hard gritty soil, and sometimes from the
narrowest of fissures in the rock, was gruelling. Angel, weary
and cross, looked back up the mountain and started to weep.
And that is how the adorable little daffodil we call Angel's
Tears got its name. It was another 'lost' Parkinson plant,
figured in his *Paradisus* under the name *Narcissus juncifolius flore
albo reflexo*.

On 19 May they reached Segovia, where even Peter Barr
found it 'Too hot to go about. So I remained indoors and
finished my letter for home.'

There was one more daffodil discovery before they got to
Madrid, *Narcissus triandrus concolor* of fragrant clusters of dainty
little drooping flowers of a delicate creamy primrose. Then it
was back to England.

In 1893 Peter Rudolph was sent by his father to Simon de
Graaff's nursery at Leiden to learn the technique of bulb
propagation, and on his return two years later Peter Barr took
him into the business as partner with his two other sons,
William and George. Barr & Son's golden trumpet Monarch
was in this year selling for 12 guineas a bulb. In 1896, with

the business in good hands and with Rudolph an experienced propagator, Peter Barr went off to Norway and Sweden, in the following year travelling to Sicily, Italy, Switzerland and Germany. The wild plants he found were of botanical interest only, but from Germany he brought back new cultivars of one of his favourite genera, hellebores. These were included in a list of twenty-eight varieties of the Lenten Rose, under the umbrella name of *Helleborus orientalis*. Of *H. niger* he was able to boast ten varieties.

In this same year, 1897, Peter Barr was one of the first sixty recipients of the Royal Horticultural Society's new medal commemorating the sixty years of the Queen's reign, the Victoria Medal of Honour, awarded to him for the part he had played in the development of the narcissus.

In 1898 he began a world tour that lasted seven years. Particularly he wanted to study the features and floras of Japan and South Africa. Lilies were his second love and these were lily countries. He wondered what America had in store for him. Almost immediately the tour became a vigorous campaign to interest the nation – in the shape of any and every listener – in his beloved flower, the daffodil.

It began, in fact, at Boston where he landed on 18 April. He saw the city's magnificent new horticultural hall and unique library of gardening books, went to visit two nurseries 'but was not impressed with either', and then was taken round the public park. Though it was profusely planted he looked in vain for drifts of daffodils under the trees. 'The system of naturalising bulbs in grass has not been attempted,' he wrote home in surprise, 'though bulbs would succeed. And so far only the common double Daffodils meet with a demand.' You can imagine how Peter Barr hastened to enlighten the park's superintendent, in his forceful descriptive tongue drawing a picture of what the place could look like in spring, sheeted with gold.

He spent a year in the United States and Canada, visiting most of the chief cities, parks and nurseries, everywhere being hailed as The Daffodil King. In Washington he found much to interest him. The State Department of Agriculture was a perfect beehive of scientific men, with a forestry office, another for the study of injurious insects, a pathological section, and others. Currently the Department was agitating for the appointment of a plant biologist who would concentrate on hybridisation. Even more interesting to Peter Barr was the professor whose job it was to discover the merits, qualities and uses of seeds, bulbs, or plants not grown in America, and to introduce them to those States where they were likely to be successful. So far as bulbs were concerned, and those of daffodils in particular, as well as many other kinds of plants, Peter Barr was ready with information.

The American press took to him. In New York Leonard Barron of *Gardening* interviewed him, and in Philadelphia G. C. Watson of *The American Florist* described him as 'a hale and hearty old gentleman, spry as a cricket and carrying his seventy-two years better than many men two decades his junior'. They found him full of good stories. 'His delightful chuckle after telling one of his dryly humorous yarns is something inimitable,' Watson wrote. 'I spent three days with him at Atlantic City and found him a most agreeable and entertaining companion.' Watson wished he could reproduce some of Barr's amusing and shrewd comments 'on men and things from women and metaphysics down to dogs and black olives', but felt that he could not do him justice. The interviews always began with questions about daffodils, and in towns where there was a keen interest in horticulture Peter Barr lectured on them.

October found him in California, and at Santa Rosa The Daffodil King met The Wizard of Horticulture. This was Luther Burbank, the man who was to be honoured by his country by having a town named after him, Lutherville (where, fittingly, the American Daffodil Society was to have its headquarters). One day of every year, 7 March, his birthday, was set aside as a State holiday in his memory – Burbank Day replacing the Arbor Day of the other American States. Burbank at forty-nine was 'a pushing enterprising man', as Peter Barr described him. His early work was with potatoes, the Burbank potato commemorating this period, but when Peter Barr visited his garden it was first to see his plum trees, one with not less than 500 grafts. The Wizard was also hybridising lilies, though it did not seem to Peter Barr that he was working on any definite lines. To the question as to whether he used Japanese, European, and American lilies, Burbank replied that he did and crossed with all of them. 'Max Leichtlin, however,' Barr wrote, 'doubts very much Burbank's success with Japanese and American lilies.' Immediately prior to Barr's visit Burbank had signed over the entire stock of his seedling lilies to one of the Eastern dealers. Many of these afterwards came to Britain, and despite Max Leichtlin's gloomy forecast there were some fine hybrids among them, borne out by Carl Purdy of Ukiah who told Peter Barr that he had seen many of them in bloom. 'So we may yet look for some good Liliums from Burbank's hybrids,' wrote Barr.

Purdy was another lily grower who also specialised in Globe Tulips (*Calochortus*) and Dog's-tooth Violets, and Peter Barr learnt that all the bulbs collected on the Pacific Coast passed through his hands. Purdy took him up into the mountains where he was experimenting in lily culture, 'which seems likely to provide America with good sound bulbs,' Barr thought. America, indeed, was to provide British gardens with the beautiful strong-growing hybrids known as the Bellingham Strain, developed when the State Department of Agriculture established a bulb station at Bellingham, near Washington. It was Carl Purdy and Luther Burbank who supplied seed and seedlings, and throughout they were closely linked with the raising of the new hybrids. Subsequently Jan de Graaff did much additional intercrossing, and it was he who marketed these hybrids under the name Bellingham Strain. These lilies are easily grown and are an ornament in any garden, grown either as individual specimens or grouped in a woodland.

Blooming in July they produce stems 7–8ft tall carrying heads of up to twenty flowers in colours ranging from clear yellow to garnet-red. Luther Burbank's own *Lilium burbankii* is still popular for its brown-freckled orange-yellow flowers.

At last reaching San Francisco, Peter Barr sailed for Japan on 24 March 1899. He left behind him an indelible memory, and where no drifts of daffodils had been they soon began to grow all over North America. Quite as if they had sprung up in his footsteps.

At Yokohama two nurseries claimed Peter Barr's attention. 'The one worked by Mr Unger,' he wrote, 'may be called the European nursery of Japan, combining, however, the finest of the Japanese cultures.' This nursery did a large trade in distributing trees and shrubs throughout the East. The nearby Yokohama Nursery Company had an immense stock of dwarfed shrubs and Japanese plants of every size and all ages. One dwarfed tree was estimated to be 500 years old, and the managing director's son told Peter Barr that they were prepared to give any purchaser its history back 400 years.

These two nurseries were the principal exporters of lilies to Europe and America, and looking over their stocks of *Lilium longiflorum*, Peter Barr drew attention to the necessity of discarding many of the varieties and working up stocks of the true *eximium* type. The Japanese lost no time in taking his advice, and even while he was there some 80,000 bulbs were put out for cultivation as a start, 'so that,' as Peter Barr wrote, 'within a few years the finest forms only will be offered'.

Besides lilies, Japan was famous for its *Iris kaempferi* (*laevigata*). The best collection grew a few miles out of Tokyo, and in writing of a visit to the iris fields Peter Barr's letter home covered four pages of notepaper (each sheet was 8½ by 5½in) and contained over 6,000 words.

A visit to the north island made a plant hunter of him, for it was there he discovered *Paeonia obovata*. Its flowers are white or rose-purple, but now only the white form is in cultivation. Then, having travelled the length of both islands, he sailed from Nagasaki for Shanghai, in Hong Kong spending several days, mainly in seeing the Botanical Garden and its director, Charles Ford. Hong Kong had just become a British colonial dependency, and Ford was busy surveying the newly ceded territory. From here Peter Barr made a brief visit to Manila en route for Queensland, where he landed at Port Darwin.

Throughout his tour of Australia he was amazed to see a vegetation utterly different from that of the rest of the world. It was not until he reached Sydney that he met up with daffodils. Here Robert Pitt, a cattle salesman, had during the great boom years spent many thousands of pounds buying hyacinths, tulips and daffodils with the idea of giving cut flowers to the city's hospitals. All the bulbous plants perished except the daffodils, and these he was still growing. There were others who were interested in the flower, and Peter Barr gave three lectures on the subject to the Horticultural Association of New South Wales. One was a chat on ancient and modern daffodils, another on the distinguishing characteristics of daffodils, and the third on the raising of new daffodils. He attended daffodil shows and noticed that trumpets were easily the favourites. When one young aspirant to fame asked him if it were possible to produce a red trumpet daffodil he gave him a formula, using the pollen of *N. incomparabilis* J. C. Backhouse and his own Santa Maria, the most orange-yellow of the trumpets. The various stages 'might occupy 20 years', he told the youth, 'but what is time when you have an object to attain?' So pleased was the Association with the 'Daffodil Chats' that it published them in a booklet and offered copies to all the horticultural societies and gardeners' associations of Australia and New Zealand. They were also available 'to the great public who have not yet joined hands in furthering and fostering the cultivation of flowers in and around the homes of our citizens and rural populations'.

Melbourne, Burnley, Adelaide, Fremantle, Perth, Albany

and Brisbane completed Peter Barr's Australian tour, and then he was off to Tasmania.

Daffodils had been brought to Tasmania by the early settlers, and from time to time new stocks arrived from England, but it was not until Peter Barr's visit that real interest in the flower was aroused. J. H. Hemsby of Hobart then started hybridising them, Petterd in Launceston, and Holgate and Hudson in Longford. Hemsby's Lilian Murdoch became a much-sought-after daffodil, and a few years after the publication in England of the first *Daffodil Year Book*, in 1913, C. E. Radcliff of Hobart became the world's leading raiser of pink-cupped varieties, for which he was awarded the Peter Barr Memorial Cup.

Then it was New Zealand, and there newspaper reporters seized upon Peter Barr as a rich source of copy. They were always on his track and 'several stirring articles were written' on the suggestions he outlined for improving the environs of Christchurch. Large areas had been retained for public parks, but their development was being held back for want of money. Barr's idea was to sell building plots and lay out a 'Park Lane' worthy of the town by the 'gentle flowing Avon', with proper carriage drives and cycle paths through the parks. He criticised the planting of Lombardy poplars as being out of harmony with the native plants. But the Christchurch people bore him no ill will, and asked him to 'talk Daffs' to their enthusiastic amateur gardeners. At Dunedin he gave another daffodil talk.

His next move was to Fiji, Samoa and Tonga. On a visit to the Fiji Botanic Garden he saw many variegated coleuses which the curator informed him had all been collected wild 'from the Bush', whereupon the veteran traveller asked whether it would be possible to beg some seeds as a starting point. He got them, and from these came the shrubby plants we grow today in our greenhouses, with leaves brilliantly coloured crimson, bronze, copper, apricot, pink and yellow.

He had sailed to Fiji in a boat of the New Zealand Steamship Company. His next tour was in a different class of steamer, employed for conveying missionaries and their goods to and fro among the islands. This time these were Lord Howe's Island, Norfolk Island (home of the pine of that name, *Araucaria excelsa*), then to New Caledonia and the New Hebrides. With him was a Melbourne nurseryman by the name of Cheeseman, and on the return journey the two of them went on an expedition on Norfolk Island 'and discovered several plants of interest and commercially valuable'. Unfortunately we do not know what these plants were.

It was now South Africa. He arrived at Cape Town on 8 August 1901, and had to remain there until 1 October of the following year. Between the two dates martial law had forbidden travel (it was soon after Mafeking). He then made a six months' tour through Natal, the Transvaal and Orange River Colony. But his time was not wasted. He gave a long lecture on daffodils to the Sea Point Horticultural Society, and another on 'Lilies of the World', urging lily enthusiasts to grow their bulbs for export and recommending a list of suitable varieties. 'In the short run from England to the Cape there should be no difficulty in getting out the bulbs of lilies in fine condition.' Then, with the industry started: 'Soon millions of bulbs could be shipped to London.' He gave advice on how the bulbs should be packed, and addressed himself also to amateur gardeners. 'The only lily I have seen growing in the gardens about Cape Town is L. longiflorum eximium.' By the time he left South Africa he had everybody lily-minded and daffodil-minded. He bore home with him stapelias, a curious genus of leafless succulents with bell-shaped flowers of lurid colours. The largest he collected had flowers 10in in diameter.

Sailing from Cape Town in March 1903 he was back in England two months later, now seventy-seven years old, and it was home to find that the daffodil which bore his name, Peter Barr, the finest and largest pure white trumpet of its day, was selling for 50 guineas a bulb.

He moved to Kirn on the Clyde to live with his widowed sister Jane, going off in December to visit Egypt, Palestine and

Greece. But this was a sightseeing holiday, and he returned again to Kirn. Not to retire from his gardening activities, however. In 1907 when his sister died he moved to live at The Hermitage, Kirn, at the age of eighty-one building himself a detached greenhouse, a potting shed, and a sitting-room which could be comfortably warmed. It was not too late in life for the active Peter Barr to study a new floral field, and he had never been quite easy in his mind about the identity of those primroses, cowslips and oxlips which his old friend (on paper) John Parkinson had described in his *Paradisus*. Now he made a remarkable collection of several thousand different primulas including all the old ones like Jackanapes-on-Horseback, Hose-in-a-Hose, and the little semi-double Primrose Greene which he believed to be unique and gave away only to special folks. There were feathered polyanthuses and cowslips, indeed all shapes and forms of these humble plants, and in one of his charming letters, which he alone seemed to know how to write, he remarked wistfully: 'I wonder who will plant my grave with Primroses.'

He went up to London regularly to attend the RHS meetings, a kenspeckle figure in his Glengarry bonnet, still spry and genial, and full of his usual fun. Then in September 1909 while on a visit to his youngest son, George, he had a sudden heart attack. He had spent a busy day calling on his London friends, in the evening dining with his family. He died in the early hours of Friday 17 September.

Peter Barr is commemorated in a lily bearing his name, in a nerine of glistening rosy flowers with a sparkling golden sheen, and in the pure white daffodil that won a First Class Certificate in 1902, as well as in the handsome Peter Barr Memorial Cup awarded each year by the Narcissus Committee to anyone who in their opinion has done work of some kind on behalf of his favourite flower.

His friend Frederick William Burbidge put into words what could be no finer epitaph when, in a letter of 10 January 1888, he wrote to him: 'You certainly have influenced a few men to wander into the fields of modern Asphodels, and your children will not need to put up a tombstone to your memory, because you will be remembered in the heart of everyone who sees or looks upon a Daffodil, for all time.'

Page 141 Ernest Henry Wilson, greatest of all the plant hunters, with a group of his beautiful Regal lilies, discovered in a valley in China. He is wearing his robes of Doctor of Science

Page 142 (above) Kurume Azaleas in the Royal Horticultural Society's Garden at Wisley, Surrey. Introduced from Japan, they went first to the Arnold Arboretum in Massachusetts; (below) the scarlet lantern heps of the climbing *Rosa moyesii* follow large single flowers of dusky red. E. H. Wilson discovered it in Western China in 1903

5

'CHINESE' WILSON AND HIS 1,500 INTRODUCTIONS 1876–1930

The great James Veitch, founder of the famous Chelsea nursery, must have had a streak of pessimism in his nature. It was he who, in 1858, advised the Royal Horticultural Society to wind up its affairs. Or perhaps it was wisdom, for he added that another society should be formed with a charter on an enlarged basis, which would be better adapted to the existing state of horticulture.

But his son James Herbert Veitch was more than pessimistic in 1899 when he engaged young Ernest Henry Wilson to travel in China as his collector. 'My boy,' he is reported as saying to him, 'stick to the one thing you are after, and do not spend time and money wandering about. Probably almost every worth-while plant in China has now been introduced into Europe.'

The 'one thing' Wilson was sent to get was the almost legendary Dove or Handkerchief Tree. He returned after eleven years of wandering in China, having introduced no fewer than 1,500 plants hitherto unknown.

E. H. Wilson was born on 15 February 1876 at Chipping Campden in Gloucestershire, the eldest son of Henry and Annie Wilson. From boyhood showing a love of gardening, he left school to become an apprentice in Hewitt's nurseries at Solihull, Warwickshire, in 1892 when he was sixteen being recommended to the Curator of the Birmingham Botanical Gardens as a promising young gardener. The hours were long, but he was eager to know his subject and after the day's work he attended Birmingham's Technical School where there were excellent facilities for studying botany. He did so well that he won the Queen's Prize at the examination held by the Board of Education. It was now Kew, the goal of all young botanists and gardeners. He went to the Royal Botanic Gardens in January 1897 and was soon winning recognition for his work in the garden and lecture room. After a year there his love of botany decided him to become a teacher in the subject, and with this intention he entered the Royal College of Science at South Kensington.

This was in October 1898. The year was the turning point in his life.

Out in China, at Ichang, a port on the Yangtsze River 1,000 miles from the sea at a point where the mountain barrier cut off the plain, was an Englishman by the name of Augustine Henry. He was attached to the Imperial Maritime Customs and was an amateur botanist. In 1888 his chief, Sir Robert Hart, had given him special leave to vary the monotony of his duties by collecting for Kew, and he made two long expeditions, the first into the mountains south-east of the river, the second into the higher and wilder mountains to the north. Lately, on a fortnight's business trip when again he had penetrated the mountains, he had been appalled to see how the country was being deforested. The Chinese seemed to take delight in felling trees to no purpose, and they burned endless quantities of timber to make charcoal. Whole mountains, once covered with forests, were now denuded. Henry had already urged Kew to send out a professional collector. He now wrote that it was urgent. Everything indicated that the region was the central point from which a flora had spread over Asia. It would soon be too late to investigate. (Wilson was to confirm Augustine Henry's theory, establishing a direct affinity between the floras of China and America. For the first time in history he discovered a species of *Symphoricarpus* outside the American continent, and found the

Eastern-Asian form of *Dipylleia cymosa* to be almost identical with that of the Allegheny Mountains. His explanation was that in pre-glacier times there was complete land connection between Asia and America, and that an exchange of plants took place in northern latitudes.)

Particularly Henry mentioned to Kew the wonderful tree he had seen ten years before, on his first expedition – *Davidia involucrata*, named after Père Armand David, the French missionary who had first discovered it. Henry wrote enthusiastically about it, one of the strangest sights he had ever seen in China, recalling how as he rode up a river valley one day he saw *Davidia* in full blow on the other side, waving its innumerable ghost handkerchiefs. He urged William Thiselton-Dyer, Kew's Director, to tell collectors to look out for it.

Kew had no funds to finance expeditions. Henry wrote to Charles Sprague Sargent of Harvard's Arnold Arboretum, and with an encouraging reply he worked out routes and costs. Sargent wanted Henry to lead the expedition himself, but by now Henry's consuming thought was to quit China for ever and go home. He was thirty-eight. Exploration was for a younger man, he declared.

Then, unexpectedly, came word from Thiselton-Dyer. He had succeeded in arousing the interest of Veitch & Sons, and they were sending out a Kew-trained man. This was Ernest Henry Wilson, whom Kew's Director had hauled out of college when James Herbert Veitch asked him to recommend a good young botanist who might do well in China as a collector of seeds and living plants.

In preparation Wilson spent six months at the Veitch nurseries at Coombe Wood, learning under George Harrow their trade and requirements. He left England in April of the following year, not the first man Veitch & Sons had sent to China. Charles Maries had preceded him twenty years before, and had failed miserably in his task. He was high-handed with the natives who, resenting his attitude, destroyed his collections. Some things did reach home, among them *Primula obconica*, and

Loropetalum chinense and its relative *Hamamelis mollis*, finest of all the Wych Hazels. But there could have been many more plants to his credit. James Veitch hoped that his new collector would do better.

Wilson, now twenty-three years old, first visited America, spending five days at the Arnold Arboretum at Boston, Massachusetts, studying the latest techniques in collecting seeds and plants and the packing of them for despatch on what would be a long journey home. The visit also laid the foundations of a friendship with the Arboretum's director, who made him welcome at his own beautiful gardens at Brookline. One day Sargent was to appoint Wilson as his right-hand man.

Sailing from San Francisco Wilson reached Hong Kong late in 1899 and travelled through French Indo-China to Szemao in the south-west corner of Yunnan, near the border with Burma. Here Augustine Henry was temporarily based, and Wilson was to learn from him the location of the Handkerchief Tree. It was a nightmare journey. Suspected of being a spy he was held for weeks in the fever-haunted town of Laokia while Europeans around him died like flies. Then on his way up the Red River, he had an opium addict as boatman and they were nearly wrecked on some rocks. But at last he met the man whom, with his plain steel-rimmed spectacles and soup-strainer moustache, people at first enjoyed as a 'character' and soon learned to love and respect. He was wise in the ways of China and gave his young visitor much practical advice, a valuable insight into the Chinese character, and a sketch-map showing the exact location of the tree he had seen twelve years ago and never forgotten.

They left Szemao together, Wilson accompanying his new friend to Meng-tze where Henry had been summoned to take charge, then making his way to the coast and collecting as he went. For there was more to China than *Davidia involucrata*, he discovered. His first consignment to Veitch included *Jasminum primulinum*, the pretty greenhouse plant of bright yellow flowers, and the magnificent *Magnolia delavayi* whose name com-

memorated Jean Marie Delavay, the French missionary, who
with Pères Armand David, Paul Guillaume Farges and Jean
André Soulié had been in the field before him. They had discovered many plants of horticultural merit and whenever
possible had sent home seeds, though comparatively few survived. More formidable was the record of Robert Fortune
whom the Horticultural Society sent out in 1843. In his eighteen
years in the Far East Fortune had sent back about 190 species,
many of them among the best-known plants in our gardens
today. The first weigela (*W. rosea*) was his discovery, the
Japanese Anemone and the Winter Jasmine, with camellias,
peonies, roses and other lovely plants. But Fortune was no
hunter in the wilds. Nearly all the plants he collected were
tried favourites of the Chinese and obtained from Chinese
gardens.

At Hai-phong Wilson found a boat for Shanghai and there
equipped himself with a houseboat and sailed in it the 1,000
miles up the Yangtze-Kiang to Ichang. This was to be his home
in his first years of plant hunting, a practical idea giving him
security as well as independence. A house he could move at will
was an important consideration, for China was in the throes of
the Boxer riots, anti-Christian murders and wholesale massacres
everyday news.

It was February when he arrived at Ichang. He waited till
April when the davidia tree would be in flower, and meanwhile got together a plant-hunting team, hiring some of
Augustine Henry's trained collectors and making some pre-
liminary excursions. The finding of the tree was a sad anti-
climax. He reached the spot where it should be and, not finding
it, asked some natives if they could show it to him. They
pointed to a stump, and then to a rude cabin built of its timber.

But luck was with him. A few weeks later he came on more
davidias. They were tall, with blossoms only at the top. To
photograph them it was necessary to climb another tree to a
height of almost 50ft, the camera being hauled up on a rope.
(Everywhere that Wilson went he carried his camera, a bulky

one with glass plates and a tripod. He amassed a monumental collection of photographs unique in scientific interest.)

Above Ichang the Yangtze ceased to be wide and calm. For 100 miles it ran turbulently through narrow gorges whose sheer cliffs on either side were sometimes 1,000ft high. Here in the glens and on the towering crags grew the floral wealth of Ichang. The variety of flowering shrubs was astonishing. First to bloom in the early spring was Fortune's *Daphne genkwa* which grew everywhere among rocks and boulders, in partial shade and exposed to the scorching sun. Its companion of the season was the white-flowered *Coronaria sinica* looking like patches of snow. Later Wilson collected its seeds, though it did not prove of much garden value.

It was the exception in a rich harvest of plants that became instant favourites when the Veitch nurseries distributed them. There were buddleias, one given his name with bright rose-lilac flowers larger than those of any other variety, and one named after Père David which Wilson liked to call the Summer Lilac: it is the handsomest of the buddleias and familiar to us all with its long panicles of violet-purple and deep orange eyes. There were three honeysuckles: *Lonicera pileata*, the Privet Honey-suckle with yellowish white flowers and attractive fruits; the white-flowered late-blooming *L. maacki podocarpa*, and *L. tragophylla* of bright yellow flowers followed by red fruits of which Wilson wrote: 'Planted in a partially shady place and trained to a stout pole, or better still set at the foot of a decidu-ous tree and let ramble at will, this species presents a beautiful sight when in flower.' There were two ligularias, *L. wilsoniana* and *L. clivorum*, dramatic when their big leaves and heads of yellow and orange-yellow ray florets were mirrored in water. (The following year brought him another, which was to bear Veitch's name, of clear yellow flowers and dark green leaves 12in or more across.) Meanwhile his introduction of *Partheno-cissus thomsonii* was a gift to those who value colourful autumn foliage, the climbing vine whose leaves turn reddish-purple, with its richly apparelled sister *Ampelopsis chaffanjonii* and elegant cousin *A. micans* of dark shining leaves, purplish stalks and dark blue fruits. *Berberis julianiae* was to prove a good hedging plant, densely evergreen with spiny stems, with a bonus of yellow flowers slightly scented and copper-tinted young growth. Of the prickly-leaved scarlet-fruited *Ilex pernyi*, Wilson declared: 'Neither man nor beast could face a hedge made of this species!' Among other climbers were *Actinidia chinensis*, called by the Chinese 'Yang-tao', whose creamy-white flowers were followed by large fruits dubbed 'Wilson's Gooseberries' by the European residents in China to whom he introduced them, and three now well-known clematis. Who does not delight in *Clematis montana rubens* with its shower of rosy flowers that hang in an arras over walls, and the evergreen *armandii* of fragrant white clusters? Wilson thought highly of another he added to the genus, *montana wilsonii*, for its masses of fragrant white flowers in June.

Ichang did not possess a great number of trees but did produce many different varieties. One of Wilson's prizes was *Catalpa fargesii*, now one of our best midsummer flowerers with its conspicuous lilac-pink blossoms spotted with red-brown and stained with yellow, seven to fifteen together in a corymb. It was growing up to 60ft tall. Smaller was the Ichang Lemon (*Citrus ichangense*) which produced lemon-like fruit. The Chinese made tea from the leaves of a particular crab apple, *Malus theifera* which has been renamed *M. hupehensis*. Wilson was very fond of this discovery and recommended it highly. It is a good all-rounder, its stiff ascending branches foaming in May and June with fragrant blossom, soft pink in bud and opening white, followed by yellow fruits. Still rare in cultivation, though its red fruits and leaves are attractive in autumn, is the euonymus he found on this trip, *E. sanguineus* whose young shoots and leaves are tinged with purple. Of the same young colouring was the Winter Hazel *Corylopsis veitchiana*, named after his employer, a beautiful shrub with fragrant primrose-yellow flowers and conspicuous red anthers.

And still they came: three shrubby cotoneasters giving colourful leaves and fruits to autumn: *acutifolius villosulus* of shining black fruits; the trailing *dammeri*, useful for the rock garden, with fruits of sealing-wax red, and *dielsianus* growing 8ft tall and crowded with round red fruits among brilliantly tinted leaves.

As to the davidia which he had been sent to get, Wilson returned to the place where he had found the trees and gathered seeds. Incidentally, when you see the 'white handkerchiefs' of a Davidia in Britain they will be among the fresh green leaves. Augustine Henry and E. H. Wilson saw them without the leaves, for in China the big white bracts appear first, among the bare branches. Henry thought they were like treefuls of fluttering white doves.

Wilson now went to Chungking in Szechuan, a journey of 400 miles that took a month. Travelling up-river was painfully slow because of rapids, swift currents and other difficulties that impeded navigation. On this stretch of the Yangtze are 1,000 rapids and dangerous rocks, according to the Chinese Gazetteer, which also records that of the vast fleet of boats continually plying up and down, some 500 are wrecked every year. Foreigners were apt to level criticism at the Chinese boatmen: Wilson found them careful and thoroughly competent. The boats might look queer, but their balanced rudder and turret were the outcome of generations of experience. He made the journey many times up and down these 400 miles, once, however, joining the 500 victims when his craft was sunk and he lost his camera with boxes of precious negatives that could never be replaced. In the books he wrote of his travels Wilson played down such incidents, and his narrow escapes from death were many. 'Nothing more than a severe wetting,' was the sort of comment he made. He disliked heroics. What mattered was the getting – amidst whatever dangers and difficulties – of the wonderful plants that inhabited the river and mountain regions, the lilies that filled valley after valley, the shrubs that put forth fragrant flowers and colourful berries, which were new and would soon enhance English gardens, the glorious trees and the climbers that festooned them – wistarias and honeysuckles, roses and clematis. Roses were plentiful everywhere, in April making the greatest show of any one kind of flower. He wrote that 'To walk through a glen in the early morning or after a slight shower, when the air is laden with the soft delicious perfume from myriads of rose blossoms, is truly to walk through an earthly paradise.'

Nearly all the towns and villages in western China were built on the banks of rivers, these being highways for traffic. Inland were roads of two kinds, paved and unpaved. Those connecting the Imperial capital with the capitals of the provinces were few in number and in Wilson's day sadly neglected. Here and there floods had swept them away, and often the paving blocks were stolen for house-building. In rainy weather stretches of mud made them almost impassable. Lesser roads were mere tracks, but at least they criss-crossed the country in every direction, even in the most sparsely populated regions. Without them it would have been impossible for Wilson to have traversed some of the most interesting parts of China.

When travelling he went fully equipped with a bed, bedding, food, cooking paraphernalia 'and *insect-powder*'. On land he rode in a sedan chair, the recognised mode of travel for foreigners, not so much as a luxury but as a symbol to command respect. He and his team of coolie collectors, bearers and head boy put up for the night at inns 'usually very filthy, and in season abounding in mosquitoes, creeping things, and stinks, the latter being always in evidence'. It was not possible to use tents. As Wilson wrote: 'The Chinese do not understand tents, and it is unwise to try innovations in a land where people are unduly inquisitive.'

His 1901 travels yielded another rich harvest. He had his own favourites among plants, which he called his 'pets'. One was *Kolkwitzia amabilis* which he named the Beauty Bush. No wonder, for it is a lovely and graceful shrub, hardy and adaptable too, whose drooping branches are mantled in May and June with bell-shaped flowers, soft pink with a yellow throat. Another was *Acer griseum*, now one of the most attractive of all our small trees with its papery bark of glistening cinnamon-red that peels off to reveal an orange underbark, and with leaves gorgeously coloured in autumn. To Wilson it was 'the gem of all'. Of another shrub he found he wrote: 'With its masses of ornamental flowers and fruits and fine autumnal tints *Stranvaesia undulata* is more than ordinarily attractive and useful.' His introduction now bears the specific name *davidiana*, with *undulata* as a varietal name describing its waved leaves. It has pure white flowers and brilliantly crimson fruits.

He crossed the Hupeh-Szechuan frontier at 7,000ft, intending to explore the valleys around Fang-hsien, and a glance at the map shows what an uninhabited region it is. He had to turn back because of lack of supplies, and his second attempt in 1907 had no better results. It was not until the following year that he succeeded in completing a route.

Meanwhile new discoveries rewarded him. There was the small rare tree *Meliosma veitchiorum*. Remarkable for its large pinnate leaves, Wilson recommended it as an excellent shade tree. Its prominent winter buds, fragrant creamy flowers and violet-coloured fruits were other recommendations. Twelve years before, Augustine Henry had discovered *Lilium leucanthum chloraster* of wide funnel-shaped blooms, yellow inside and greenish outside. He sent bulbs to England but the stock perished. Wilson was now able to reintroduce it. He found another of Henry's plants, a neat privet, and yet another, the little *Sarcococca ruscifolia* which delights in shade and produces its tiny fragrant white flowers in the earliest days of spring. New was the sun-loving Hydrangea Vine, *Schizophragma integrifolium*, that split-personality of a plant which starts as a clinging climber and then throws out erect branches. In the previous year, 1900, he had discovered five new rhododendrons. Now he found seven more, including *R. sutchuenense*, one of the finest of all the Chinese species. He discovered new trees: *Liriodendron chinense*, the Chinese form of the Tulip Tree, and the Chinese Yellow Wood, remarkably beautiful with its panicles of white and pink flowers. He found a new conifer, *Abies fargesii*, now one of the best Asiatic Silver Firs in cultivation, and the pretty little *Daphne retusa* whose fragrant rose-purple flowers come in May and June.

The year 1901 was sliding into 1902. Before he left for England Wilson added another beautiful tree. It was *Acer davidii*, loved for its green and white striped bark and the green and yellow fruits which hang all along its branches among yellow, red and purple leaves. He took with him seeds of a new primrose which was given his name, but it was a long time before *Primula wilsonii* made up its mind to flower. It did not do so until 21 May 1906, a date that was to be one of celebration.

He arrived home in April 1902 and on 8 June married Helen Ganderton of Edgbaston. At Coombe Wood he was delighted to see rows of healthy plants grown from the seeds he had collected, and Veitch lost little time in sending his valuable plant hunter off on a second expedition to China, this time in search of a wonderful yellow poppywort, *Meconopsis integrifolia*. Wilson left England in 1903, this time to spend two and a half years on journeys that took him 2,000 miles into the interior, following the Min River to the borderland of Tibet and climbing to the summits of sacred Mount Omei and its sister mountain, Wa shan.

The borderland, a wild rugged land, was an extension of the Himalayas, a series of stupendous mountain ranges separated by narrow valleys. Few of the tribesmen had ever seen a white man. Wilson found it interesting that up in the heights the flora had adapted itself to withstand drought. Many of the shrubs were spiny, and most had leaves either small or covered with a dense felt of hairs. The commonest plants were species of the silvery-grey southernwoods, of which Wilson had introduced *Artemisia lactiflora* in 1901. Now, far up on the sides of the cliffs, he ended his search for the wonderful yellow poppywort *Meconopsis integrifolia*. The most gorgeous alpine in all the world, he described it.

In the valleys berry-bearing shrubs were the feature, mainly barberries and cotoneasters. He introduced eleven species of each. Roses were common. One he discovered in this year was that graceful climbing favourite of long sprays of single crimson flowers bossed with gold, *Rosa moyesii*, without which no garden is complete. Another was the magnificent *R. sinowilsonii*, the epithet deriving from his nickname 'Chinese Wilson' which he did not at all dislike. It has panicles of large white flowers and superb foliage deep glossy green above, beneath flushed with purple. Yet another was the charming rose (named after that famous gardener Ellen Willmott), of rosy-pink flowers, orange-red hips and straw-yellow prickles.

Some of the valleys were the homes of beautiful lilies, and curiously each valley had a species or variety of its own. In the Tung Valley grew *Lilium sargentii*, in the Min Valley that most glorious of lilies which, had he introduced no other plant, would have assured Wilson's place in horticultural history, *L. regale*. Indeed, Wilson once stated that he would rest his reputation on the Regal Lily, which grew very well and had a place of honour in his garden. Incidentally, it did not receive the name until 1912 when it was recognised as a new species. Up till then the 300 bulbs Wilson sent home in 1904 were flowered and distributed by Veitch as *L. myriophyllum*, a separate species discovered by Delavay.

Wilson marvelled to see his trumpet beauty luxuriating in rocky crevices sunbaked throughout the year, and filling acres of the valley floor. There were lilies everywhere. He wrote that in late June and July it was possible to walk for days through a veritable wild garden dominated by these beautiful flowers.

In boggy ground he found a fascinating rhubarb, *Rheum alexandrae*, with tall spikes of pale yellow bracts overlapping one another like tiles on a house roof. The deutzia is a handsome shrub and easily grown. Père David had collected dried specimens of *D. longifolia*, but now Wilson was the introducer of the living plant. Its flower-colours varying from rose-purple to crimson-pink, he chose the best colours and largest form and called it *veitchii*. This variety is now the aristocrat of the group. Another good shrub, excellent for a sunny rockery, was a new *Berberis* which was given the name *wilsoniae* for its discoverer's wife. It has golden flowers and coral-red fruits. There was a magnificent new sorbus (*S. megalocarpa*), remarkable for its brown-purple twigs, crimson sticky buds like those of a horse-chestnut and brown fruits like small partridge eggs, and a new willow which he took at first to be a magnolia. This was *Salix magnifica* which produces catkins a foot long. He introduced it as living plants in 1908. And these were only some of his treasures.

On 13 October he began his ascent of the sacred Mount Omei, a gigantic upthrust of hard limestone rising sheer from the plain to a height of nearly 11,000ft above sea level. There were two floral regions of the mountain, the lower zone up to 6,000ft where plants enjoyed a warm-temperate climate, and the upper zone with plants requiring cool-temperate conditions. The contrast between the two was as startling as the scenery. Below, until lost in the clouds, was a mass of rich green summer vegetation: above were autumn tints from pale yellow to the most glorious shades of crimson. The whole mountain was bathed in sunlight. A never-to-be-forgotten scene, Wilson recorded. Plant-wise it was equally rewarding. He gathered thirteen species of rhododendron, four new primulas and, in one day, over sixty species of fern. On the surrounds of the mountain top he found *Rosa omeiensis* growing among dense scrub. In the warmer climate below it was in bright red fruit, but up here was still massed with single white flowers. Trailing over the scrub was the clematis he had introduced in 1900, *C. montana wilsonii*.

From the summit of Omei shan he looked across to Wa shan, the sacred one's sister. This mountain resembled a Noah's Ark, broadside on, perched high among the clouds. He had climbed it in July with his dog and a guide. Above 6,000ft were rodgersias, spiraeas, astilbes and pedicularis, and growing among them bushes of a philadelphus of fragrant bell-shaped flowers. Named after him it is now renamed *P. subcanus*. On the plateau, 8,500ft up, he found a tree-like shrub with large lustrous leaves and white florets, *Hydrangea xanthoneura wilsonii*, one of the delightful lacecaps. Then from 10,000ft to the summit came the rhododendrons in thousands and hundreds of thousands. The wealth of their blossom almost hid the foliage: crimson, bright red, flesh-coloured, silvery pink, yellow, and pure white. They grew everywhere, finding root-holds even on wild crags and cliffs. Some were growing on the fallen trunks of Silver Fir, and some were epiphytic. Beneath them was a pretty carpet of sphagnum moss. He discovered sixteen different kinds varying from giants up to 50ft tall to diminutive plants of only a few inches.

Then began the climb to the summit. There were three precipices to be scaled, and each had to be ascended by means of a long wooden ladder. 'Up these I carried my dog,' Wilson wrote, 'never thinking of the descent. On returning he became frightened, and though we blindfolded him he struggled much and on one occasion his struggles all but upset my balance. It requires all one's nerve to mount a ladder with no balustrade, fixed to a cliff 40 ft vertical, and on either side a yawning abyss lost in the clouds.' No wonder he was 'heartily thankful when safe ground was reached'. But the summit was worth seeing, thickets of rhododendrons alternating with glades carpeted with anemones and primulas. Edward Colbourne Baber, the first foreigner to climb Wa shan, described the summit as 'the most charming natural park in the world'. It was a fruitful expedition for Wilson. In four days' botanising on the mountain he added some 220 species to his collection. The work was excessively hard, and once when he slipped on some loose débris he was saved from being precipitated over a steep cliff by the presence of mind of a coolie who just happened to be near him. Wilson botanised on many mountains in different parts of China, but none did he find richer in cool-temperate plants and flowering shrubs than Wa shan.

In 1904 he followed the great north road across the plain of Chengtu to Mien Chou, then on another recognised highway to Chungpa and Lungan Fu. The inns were, as usual, malodorous and vermin-infested. But new rewards awaited him. On a day's struggle to the 4,000ft summit of the pass leading across the Tu-ti-liang the outstanding feature was the abundance of cercidiphyllum trees, that beauty of cordate leaves which in autumn turn to golden coins. They grew on the moist slopes on both sides of the range, and some were enormous, one measuring 55ft in girth. Later he collected ripe seeds, and *Cercidiphyllum japonicum sinense* is now one of the loveliest trees we can grow.

It was a journey through savage mountains of sublime scenery and wonderful flora. He climbed to a height of 16,000ft where only juniper grew. Two thousand feet below, the flowers were in plenty, the commonest being the beautiful *Meconopsis punicea* of dark scarlet nodding heads.

Wherever he went new treasures appeared before him. He collected two orchids: *Cymbidium wilsonii* of light-green flowers and yellow lip spotted with red-brown, and the dwarf *Cypripedium tibeticum* of huge dark red flowers. Twenty-five miles above San-tsze-yeh a torrent heavily surcharged with lime descended from the eternal snows, leaving thick encrustations all along its course. Here stood the Temple of the Dragon Prince, where priests had led the stream in and out of some fifty semicircular dams. All were at slightly different levels, and each – according to the depth it had been dug reflected different colours: azure, pink, green, creamy white or purple. Right by the water's edge he discovered *Arctostaphylos alpina ruber*, a tiny shrub with red fruit. A pretty little plant, 4–6in high, it had never before been found in China.

Wilson sailed for England in December 1904, taking with him yet more plants collected in this year. One was *Primula cockburniana* of orange flowers 1in across. Wilson declared that this primrose had more character in the turn of its leaf than many others had about them altogether. Primroses were his favourite flowers, and in China where there are ninety different kinds he saw them at their best, often carpeting immense tracts of country. The very first plant to bear his name was *Primula wilsonii*, and on 21 May 1906 when his daughter was born it put forth its first purple blossom, as if in celebration. The baby was christened Muriel Primrose.

The two trips for Veitch had produced 2,000 lots of seeds and plants, and such a vast amount of herbarium material (5,000 specimens) that Kew asked him to come as temporary assistant, to help sort and identify them.

In January 1906 Wilson took a post as botanical assistant at the Imperial Institute, the sort of job he had been intending to do when he left Kew. He was there only a few months, for again fate intervened to send him to China. This time it was for the Arnold Arboretum and some private subscribers who were anxious to have a share of Wilson plants. Among them was Ellen Willmott. He left for Boston in December, and at the end of that month sailed for Shanghai. In November he had been awarded the Veitch Medal in recognition of his services to horticulture.

The particular object of this expedition was to locate trees and shrubs of value to American gardens, and he spent much of his time in western Hupeh, basing himself at Ichang as before. One of the very first shrubs he discovered was not only a new species but the single species of a new genus to which he gave the name of his new patron Charles Sprague Sargent. In Britain *Sargentodoxa cuneata* of fragrant racemes of greenish-yellow flowers is a tender subject, needing the protection of a wall. A new barberry, evergreen and with clusters of yellow flowers, he called *Berberis sargentiana*, also naming for Sargent a pale violet hydrangea whose foliage was particularly handsome, dark green with a velvety lustre. Ellen Willmott was to get her share of the spoils, in her garden at Warley Place, Essex, raising the delightful plumbago *Ceratostigma willmottiana* (1908), *Corylopsis willmottiae* (1909), *Lilium davidii* var. *willmottiae* (1910), *Paeonia obovata* var. *willmottiae* (1915), and *Rosa willmottiae* (1904), which last she treasured, for she was a great rosarian and wrote a monograph on the genus. E. H. Wilson did not forget his wife. In a wild entrancing gorge above Ichang, at a time when 'the Musk Roses were the flowers of the day', he

Page 159 (right) Reginald Farrer who transformed rock gardening, sweeping away the 'Almond Pudding' of upright stones and creating natural rock structures where alpine plants could feel at home

(left) Gentiana farreri of pale blue trumpets, one of the alpine treasures Farrer introduced. Here is his painting of it

Page 160 (left) *Primula calliantha* of purplish-rose flowers, from a sketch by Reginald Farrer. He drew all his new treasures in their natural setting, just as he made a natural setting for the live plants in his rock garden; (*below*) the incomparable winter-blooming *Viburnum fragrans* of pale pink heads of flowers, which Farrer discovered growing wild in South Kansu

found a single white fragrant beauty that was new, and named it *Rosa helenae*.

Outstanding for garden value is *Cornus kousa*, introduced from Japan in 1875. Wilson now found its Chinese counterpart, equally beautiful and more hardy. In June its masses of white flowers lie along its spreading branches like snow. He added *Cercis racemosa*, of the genus known in America as the Redbuds. It is handsome with its hanging rosy-pink pea flowers, freely produced in Britain in May, though not on young trees.

What a wealth of beauty the cotoneasters give us in their varied forms! Wilson was always coming upon new ones, in 1907 finding the pink-flowered *C. divaricatus* of stunning autumn colouring, the graceful *hupehensis* whose single fruits are like scarlet tear-drops, and the *rugosus* hybrid of *salicifolius*. Another hybrid of this invaluable evergreen parent was a 1908 discovery, *flocossus* of narrow polished leaves, downy beneath, poised on slender fanlike stems. *C. horizontalis perpusillus* was a charming dwarf form of herring-bone branchlets giving rich autumn colours in berry and leaf.

Viburnum henryi was another valuable discovery this year. 'A more highly decorative shrub would be hard to find,' Wilson wrote of it. His ornamental cherry *Prunus dielsiana* was an enchantment of mahogany-red bole and branches, and pink and white flowers hanging like eardrops from long downy pedicels. Another, thought to have been a Wilson find in 1907, appeared in the famous Scottish garden at Dawyck and was given that name, a small tree of shining dark brown bark, pale pink flowers and amber-red cherries.

In 1903 and again the following year he had visited Tachienlu. Now in the summer of 1908, while he was in Chengtu, he decided to make a third journey there but this time following the road from Kuan Hsien via Mongkong Ting and Romi Chango. He had read the published account of the route in the report Sir Alexander Hosie, Consul-general at Chengtu, presented to both Houses of Parliament. Sir Alexander's descriptions promised a difficult trip, but Wilson felt sure that by taking his time and only lightly burdening his men he could get through all right. Events proved him correct. Although there were many hardships to be endured, what he saw of the forests and mountain scenery, together with the quantity and variety of plants discovered and collected, amply rewarded him. He left Chengtu on 15 June with a caravan of eighteen carrying coolies, a head coolie, two handymen, an escort of two soldiers, five men to bear the two sedan chairs, and his boy.

At first it was all rivers. Not counting the streams flowing in the direction of Chengtu, they crossed five separate arms of the Min proper. The famous bamboo bridge known as the An-lan-chiao, over which the road to Mongkong Ting passed, was having its annual overhaul, so they had to cross by ferry or improvised bridges, sometimes a hair-raising experience in China. Wilson tells of an adventure in Hsin-kai-tsze where the road crossed a log bridge, again being repaired, with only two uneven logs in position. A thin rope served as a handrail on one side. Wilson's men got over safely but his dog refused to cross and had to be lashed firmly to a flat board and carried over on a coolie's back, Wilson walking behind. The dog worked himself half loose just as they reached the shore.

Then it was all ascents and descents, toiling up ridges 6,000ft up and more, coming down precipitously among loose rocks. The road over Niu-tou shan, 10,000ft, was 'vile to walk on'. In many places it was dangerous, and here and there were steps cut in the hard rock to assist the traveller. Mainly it was strewn with stones and boulders. But the mountain was remarkable for its wealth of willows. New was *Salix bockii*, a most attractive dwarf species with slender reddish twigs, greyish downy when young and in spring peppered with the bright green of emerging leaf-clusters. This is the only willow in general cultivation to bear catkins in autumn. On a later visit Wilson introduced about a dozen new willows from the locality.

The flora was very interesting, though because of a thick pall of mist he could observe only what grew alongside the road.

If it deserved the name. In several places poles had been fixed horizontally into holes made in the face of the cliffs, and decaying planks laid on these to form a pathway. Below them the river was a thundering torrent cascading over huge boulders, in a mad endeavour, it seemed to Wilson, to escape to less savage regions. Whenever the clouds lifted they saw nothing but steep mountainsides, beetling crags and more cliffs ahead of them.

On the grassy ridge leading up to the Pal-lan shan the flora was alpine in character, and Wilson was fascinated to see that most of the vigorous-growing herbs had yellow flowers. Spectacular was his gorgeous *Meconopsis integrifolia*, myriads of its huge yellow globes covering miles of the mountainside. It occurred in countless thousands even above 12,000ft, as did his other poppywort, the scarlet *punicea*.

Gaining the pass was a slow toil in a dense, driving, bitterly cold mist. Below it at an altitude of 13,700ft was the miserable hostel of Wan-jên-fên, but nearby he found the prickly evergreen oak *Quercus aquifolioides*. It shone out of the desolation, the golden-brown undersides of its leaves making it almost as beautiful as the Golden Oak of California.

The valley was relatively warm, and here he found a new bush honeysuckle, *Lonicera nitida* of creamy-white fragrant flowers. With its small shiny evergreen leaves it makes an excellent hedge if close-clipped. The commonest form is 'Ernest Wilson', the 'nitida' of the nurserymen's catalogues.

Romi Chango was a poor unwalled town of some 130 houses. But its inn was comfortable and they spent a quiet day, resting and refitting for the final stage of the journey to Tachienlu. Ahead of them, they were warned, the road was very difficult, leading through forests and over high mountains. It was hardly a road at all! Whenever their way led past a house they had to cross an open sewer. Farther on, some of the road was under water, and Wilson traversed these parts on the back of one of the soldiers, until the man stumbled and nearly gave him a ducking, after which Wilson waded. The sedan chairs were dismantled and carried over piecemeal, even then with difficulty. In many places the path actually overhung the torrent, awesome to behold when one false step meant death.

Camping at an altitude of 12,000ft, they were too cold to sleep, Wilson's dog suffering with them all and refusing to eat his supper. But at last they saw, straight ahead of them, an enormous mass of dazzling snow over 22,000ft high, and in the far distance the perpetual snows around Tachienlu. It was a sunny day and an easy road to gain their goal, a cluster of closely packed houses nestling in the valley.

As they walked into the town Wilson saw a very distinct-looking peach tree with long pointed leaves growing here and there among the rocks. 'I regard this as among the most remarkable of the discoveries I have been privileged to make,' he wrote. 'At the time, I paid no further attention to the Peach, but in 1910 I secured ripe fruit and found to my astonishment that the stones were perfectly smooth, free, and relatively small.' It was given the name *Prunus mira*, meaning the wonderful or extraordinary peach, which fits it exactly, for it is the only one with a smooth stone. Raised at the Plant Introduction Station in Maryland it went into cultivation, not only useful but beautiful with its foaming pink blossom and bright autumn leaves.

Omei shan and Wa shan have a smaller sister, Wa-wu shan, and this Wilson climbed in 1908. Rhododendrons were fairly numerous: he noted ten species and collected a new one, *R. openshawianum*, named in honour of the Rev Harry Openshaw of Yachou Fu. The road proved to be appalling. 'It is misleading and foolish to term it a road,' Wilson wrote in disgust. 'Goats would make a better pathway, did they travel it frequently.' But the scenery was grand, and among the broad-leaved trees he discovered a new horse-chestnut, *Aesculus wilsonii*, with the same long cylindrical spikes of white flowers as the Chinese Horse Chestnut but with larger leaves.

His bundles of plants grew in number and size. In 1909, among the treasures he added were two fine spiraeas, *sargentiana* and *mollifolia*, the first a graceful shrub with creamy-white flowers carried in dense corymbs along its branches in June, the other with pretty grey leaves, purplish shoots and the same habit of flowering along its branches. There was a handsome barberry of bright yellow flowers (*Berberis atrocarpa*), the beautiful white *Clematis spooneri* (now named *C. chrysocoma sericea*), a yellow and purple iris given his name, and two more rhododendrons. To say nothing of the collection he had made the year before, which included *Celastrus rugosus*, a vine with orange capsules and bright red seeds; the shrub *Indigofera amblyantha* whose shrimp-pink flowers remain in bloom all summer and autumn; the pear *Pyrus calleryana* whose non-thorny seedling Bradford was also raised at Glenn Dale, Maryland, and became a favourite street tree, sheeted with blossom in late March or early April. It also provided stock for edible pears and proved remarkably resistant to pear blight.

There were twelve new rhododendrons, and a small bushy tree of handsome lime-like leaves and pendulous catkins, *Sinowilsonia henryi*, a rare monotypic genus again commemorating the man who of all plant hunters was probably the greatest. Among other 1908 plants were *Sorbaria arborea*, the Tree Spiraea, and *Viburnum wilsonii* of oval leaves, white flowers and bright red egg-shaped fruits covered with down.

Then in April 1909 it was back to England. Wilson stayed in London until September, before returning to the Arnold Arboretum.

In the following year he left again for China, for his fourth and last visit, this time varying his route by travelling overland on the trans-Siberian railway to Peking via Moscow. He reached Ichang in May.

The fame of the wonderful Regal Lily had spread, and Professor Sargent wanted a consignment of them. So in October, when the bulbs would be ready for lifting, Wilson set off for his happy hunting ground in the Hupeh mountains.

Before then he went to Sungpang Ting to secure seeds and herbarium specimens of some new conifers he had discovered in the region. One was a Silver Fir (*Abies delavayi faxoniana*) which in cultivation did not prove satisfactory. The other two were spruces, *Picea asperata* being a medium-sized tree, lime-tolerant and very hardy, and *P. brachytyla* (*ascendens*) with grace-fully ascending branches upturned at the tips. It was the most valued timber tree in the district, and he was able to collect plenty of seeds and introduce it into Western gardens. A new shrubby elder cropped up, *Sambucus schweriniana*, 3–5ft tall. With its masses of salmon-red fruits it was a pretty sight in all the more open moist places. Large flowers of a very deep blue distinguished *Aconitum wilsonii*, the Violet Monkshood, and he collected the seeds of this and of two anemones. *A. vitifolia alba*, 4–5ft tall and bearing myriads of large attractive flowers, covered clearings and abandoned cultivated areas with seas of white, making a wonderful display. *A. hupehensis* was of the same height but with mauve flowers. Many varieties have been raised from this plant, varying in colour and form.

There was another new berberis (*B. vernae*) with dense racemes of yellow flowers and red fruit, two new cotoneasters (*C. racemiflorus soongaricus* and *C. apiculatus*), both red-fruited; and in a gorge near Hsiang-t'am in western Hupeh he found the greenhouse flower *Rehmannia angulata*, a 6ft-tall perennial carrying seven to twelve large rosy-pink flowers like foxgloves. Its local name was the Honey-Bee Flower. Across the Hupeh-Szechuan frontier he found another tall perennial, *Astilbe davidii* of long panicles of rose-pink flowers with dark blue anthers.

It was after he had crossed the Sha-mu-jen range and was coming down on the other side through birch woods, that he found a most beautiful bamboo. It was growing in thick clumps, and its golden-yellow culms sprang 5–12ft tall from dark feathery foliage. 'The handsomest bamboo I have ever seen,' commented Wilson, adding proudly, 'It has been named *Arundinaria murielae* in compliment to my daughter.'

Then came the lilies.

The trip nearly brought Wilson's life to an untimely end.

The bulbs had been dug up and made into packs to be carried on the coolies' backs down to the river where boats were waiting, when suddenly there was a sinister whispering in the air that became a rushing sound intensifying to a thunderous roar as an avalanche came sweeping down the mountainside. There was no escape. It picked up Wilson's sedan chair and hurled it hundreds of feet below to the river. Fortunately he was able to leap out. But he could not dodge the boulder that came crashing down and broke his right leg in two places below the knee. Then a mule team came pattering down the trail, a long string of forty of them, and each of the forty stepped neatly over him as he lay helpless in the road. His camera had gone with the sedan chair but fortunately he still had the tripod. Its legs made excellent splints, and he was carried back to Chengtu, a journey of three days, to be cared for by the doctors of the Friends' Presbyterian Mission. His leg healed badly at first and left him with the slight hobble ('my lily limp', he called it) which prevented his enlisting in the 1914–18 war. This he felt deeply, wanting to take an active part in it and as an Englishman, for he never relinquished his British citizenship.

From his two expeditions to China for the Arnold Arboretum, Wilson sent back 1,593 lots of seeds, 168 lots of plants and cuttings, and 65,000 herbarium specimens.

Recognition came. The Royal Horticultural Society gave him its highest award, the Victoria Medal of Honour. The Massachusetts Society awarded him its Gold Medal.

From March 1911 until the end of 1913 he was at the Arnold Arboretum sorting and classifying his collections and, with Alfred Rehder, preparing an account of his Chinese plants. This was edited by Charles S. Sargent under the title *Plantae Wilsonianae*.

In 1914, accompanied by his wife and daughter, he went to Japan. Professor Sargent had spent some months in Japan a few years before and had introduced several new plants, among them *Azalea kaempferi*. He believed there were fresh treasures to be found. Wilson was asked to pay special attention to cherry trees, and in one garden where eighty forms were grown he collected herbarium material of sixty-three named varieties. He spent February and March in southern Japan, from April to June collecting in central Japan, and in July and August he was in Hondo and Saghalin. He returned to central Japan in the autumn. The last two months of the year he spent on the island of Shikoku. Then, having collected about 2,000 distinct herbarium specimens with many duplicates, taken about 600 photographs and sent home a large collection of Japanese cherries and seeds, he returned to the Arnold Arboretum in February 1915 to arrange his Japanese collections and continue the preparation of *Plantae Wilsonianae*.

In January 1917 Wilson left for his sixth and last trip to the Far East, in February and March exploring the Liukiu Islands and in April the Bonin Islands. In May he left for Korea, making this his base and putting his daughter Muriel to school there. During the rest of the year he visited almost all the provinces and also the southern island of Quelpaert and the small Dagelet Island whose flora is closely related to that of Japan. January 1918 saw him in Formosa, visiting Mount Arison on the successful hunt for the tallest tree of Eastern Asia and counterpart of the Californian sequoia, *Taiwania cryptomerioides*. His guides on this occasion were Formosan head-hunters. He climbed Mount Morrison, Formosa's highest peak at 13,072ft. In April he returned to Japan.

And there an adventure began that was to have floral echoes all round the Western world of horticulture. It happened when he visited the city of Kurume on Kyushu Island to see a collection of 250 named kinds of azalea, a collection started by Motozo Sakamoto a century before.

In his book *Plant Hunting*, Wilson wrote:

> I was first introduced to the Kurume family in 1914, when at the invitation of my lamented friend, the late Mr H. Suzuki, the foremost

Japanese horticulturist of his time, I accompanied him to the nursery district of Hatagaya, a few miles north of Tokyo. There in a garden I saw thousands of tiny plants bearing white and coloured flowers of nearly every hue. With the courteous consent of the owner I secured a set of fragments and dried them for the Arnold Arboretum.

Now, visiting the headquarters of the family cultivating the azalea in Kurume, he wrote:

> The gardens of the two leading specialists were veritable fairylands, and I gasped with astonishment when I realised that garden-lovers of America and Europe knew virtually nothing of this wealth of beauty. Most of the plants were trained into low standards, each about 20 inches high with flattened or convex crowns some 24 inches through, and were monuments to the patience and cultural skill of the Japanese gardener. The flowers, each about one-half to three-quarters of an inch across, were in such profusion as to almost hide the leaves. They are the roguish eyes of laughing, dimpled, and blushing blossoms.

With more than 250 kinds the array was dazzling and bewildering. Wilson had two leading experts select six as the best of all. They were Takasago, Azume-kagani, Kirin, Kumo-no-uye, Kurai-no-himo and Kureno-yuki. He then made two pilgrimages: first, to see in an old garden the original plant, which had come, it was said, from the sacred Mount Kirishima; then to climb the Mount itself. At an altitude of 3,000ft above sea level he found many wild azaleas growing in volcanic soil among the rocks and on wind-swept slopes. This convinced him that the mountain was indeed the source.

The introduction of these wonderful azaleas was the dramatic climax of his plant-hunting career. He was in love with them, referring to them as 'the divine Princess Kurume' who could be assured of a lasting welcome in this land of his adoption. 'Proud am I,' he wrote, 'of being the fortunate one to introduce this exquisite damsel to the gardens of eastern North America.'

In Britain we know the Kurumes as the 'Wilson Fifty' and can see them in all their glory at Wisley, the garden of the Royal Horticultural Society in Surrey, though actually in all there were fifty-one sorts brought by him from Japan, with seeds and roots of other plants : from Korea a superb stewartia (*S. koreana*) of large white flowers, *Astilbe koreana*, two syringas (*dilitata* and *velutina*), *Forsythia ovata* and *Thuja koraiensis* found on the Diamond Mountains, *Spiraea trichocarpa*, known as the Korean Bridal Wreath, and a splendid rhododendron (*R. weyrichii*) which was too tender for Boston but succeeded well in England. Among plants from Formosa were two lilies (*Lilium speciosum gloriosoides* and *L. philippinense formosanum*) and *Pieris taiwanensis* with beautiful erect white flower-panicles like lily of the valley.

In 1919 E. H. Wilson was appointed Assistant Director of the Arnold Arboretum. His first job there was to establish closer relations between the Arboretum and other botanical institutions all over the world. No better man could have been found. Wilson was a natural diplomat. He had always got on well with people, though not sociable in the ordinary sense. In China, where unless one were sympathetic to the Chinese temperament life could be difficult, he had made lasting friends among high and low. He was sad to part with his faithful coolies, and they with him.

He went to Australia, New Zealand and Tasmania, Singapore and Penang, India, East Africa, Kenya, Rhodesia and South Africa, and England and France, combining his visits with collecting tours in these countries' forests and returning to Boston in August 1922. He was given a small office on the second floor of the administration building where he acted as a buffer for Professor Sargent, interviewing the many callers, answering innumerable questions and adding a new dimension to the Arboretum's reputation. In April 1927, on Sargent's death, he was appointed Keeper of the Arboretum, a post he was to hold for only three years. On 15 October 1930, when he and his wife were returning from a visit to their now married daughter, the car he was driving skidded on a road made slippery by fallen leaves. It swerved across the pavement, crashed through a wooden fence and dropped over a steep embankment to a field 40ft below. Mrs Wilson was killed outright, and he himself died on the way to hospital without regaining consciousness.

Wilson had many honours bestowed upon him. He became President of the Kew Guild and was awarded the Loder Rhododendron Cup by the Royal Horticultural Society which also gave him its Veitch Memorial Medal for his plant introductions and his writings. He was a prolific writer and wrote well. Of added interest and value to his books were their excellent illustrations, reproductions of photographs he had taken in almost every part of the world.

Much sought after as a lecturer by various horticultural societies, Wilson took a particular interest in the Massachusetts Horticultural Society of which he was a trustee and member of several important committees, as well as being advisory editor of its publication *Horticulture*. The Society awarded him its Centennial Gold Medal.

Ernest Henry Wilson was on the whole a quiet reserved man. He was reserved even in his literary work. Only occasionally did he allow his passionate love of nature to burst forth spontaneously, as it did in 1923 when he summed up his adventurous years of plant hunting in these words:

Sometimes friends have said, 'You must have endured much hardship wandering in out-of-the-way corners of the earth.' I have. But such count for nothing, since I have lived in Nature's boundless halls and drunk deeply of her pleasures. To wander through a tropical or temperate forest with tree trunks more stately than a gothic column, beneath a canopy of foliage more lovely in its varied forms than the roof of any building fashioned by man, the welcome cool, the music of the babbling brook, the smell of Mother Earth, and the mixed odours of a myriad of flowers – where does hardship figure when the reward is such?

6

REGINALD FARRER – PIONEER OF THE ROCK GARDEN 1880–1920

Not everybody liked Reginald Farrer. He could be outrageously rude to people, or bitingly sarcastic, as on the occasion he mocked, in print, the wealthy industrialist Frank Crisp who, when the craze for alpine plants and 'rock-work' broke over the land, outdid all others by creating in 4 acres of his garden at Friar Park, near Henley, an exact replica of the Matterhorn in 7,000 tons of millstone grit boulders eked out with Portland cement and topped with shimmering alabaster to represent the eternal snow. Farrer tactlessly used his Introduction to E. A. Bowles's *My Garden in Spring* as a platform from which to vent his ridicule of 'the very rich ... out to purchase the glories of the Alps at so much a yard', deriding 'the colour-masses laid on in pseudo-irregular blots and drifts' which was 'nothing but the carpet-bedding of our grandfathers', a form of gardening Farrer despised. His denunciation of Crisp, tacitly the butt of his scorn, stirred up the greatest horticultural scandal of the century, with the egocentric Miss Ellen Willmott handing out scurrilous broadsheets from a bookie's large leather bag at the main entrance gates to the Chelsea Show.

But we can forget all that when we come to read Reginald Farrer's books, for nobody has ever written about plants as he wrote about them, his pen flowing with poetry and charged with down-to-earth practicality. He saw plants with the eyes of a lover; he described them as he knew them in their native homes, making them live before our eyes. When we read *Among the Hills, The Dolomites, The Rainbow Bridge, On the Eaves of the World*; when we think of the plants he introduced into our gardens – exquisite primulas and many other alpines, with shrubs such as his incomparable *Viburnum fragrans* (now named *V. farreri*) and even a new tree or two; when we look at his paintings of plants, so perfectly delineating the personality of each and shown as it was growing on mountain steep against a background of snow-capped peaks; when finally we consider that it was he who founded the modern rock garden which replaced the 'cementaries' of Victorian days and gave us an altogether new form of gardening: we realise how deep is our gratitude to Reginald Farrer.

It was the ostentatious and pretentious that drew the sword of his irony: he never willingly hurt a friend. When he died, at the early age of forty, the horticultural world mourned the loss of a man who above everything had inspired people to love plants as he did, to grow them as Nature grew them; and to follow him to the hills, by proxy through his writings or in reality by booking themselves to King Laurin's Garden in the Dolomites or to the High Pyrenees.

Plants were his passion even as a small boy. Recorded is his delight at the age of three on seeing his first field of narcissus and discovering a Lady Tulip, this at Cap d'Antibes on a Continental holiday with his mother lasting eleven months, most of them spent on the Riviera. By the time he was eight he knew by heart a school book of botany and could dissect a flower with the knowledge of its component parts. Year by year his love of plants developed without a break. For, born with a hare-lip that necessitated a series of operations, his parents had him educated at Ingleborough, their home among the Yorkshire fells and one of the richest areas in Britain for native alpines. He spent some time of each day climbing and exploring them.

He was a plant hunter from the start, collecting and pressing plants, bringing back live plants to grow, identifying them with the help of Bentham and Hooker's *Handbook of the British Flora*. When he was fourteen he redesigned Ingleborough's rock garden. The fleet of gardeners did the heavy work; he superintended the placing of the stones in the natural formations he had studied in the hills. At the same age he made his début as a botanical writer by contributing to that erudite publication the *Journal of Botany* a note on the occurrence of *Arenaria gothica*, a rare species he found growing along the upper limestone level on the eastern slopes of Ingleborough. It was a plant good enough to be included in his great work, still the standard reference, *The English Rock Garden*, with *Dryas octopetala minor* from Arncliffe Clouder ('one of the very best of rock shrubs'), *Cochlearia alpina* ('the scurvy-grass of Ingleborough'), *Potentilla rupestris* ('tallish, snowy sprays; a very rare native'), *Potentilla verna* ('our own golden Alpine'), *Viola lutea* (our native yellow mountain pansy') and others.

His rock garden was a remarkable early achievement, showing that he already understood plant ecology, providing clefts for plants that naturally grew in crevices, and moist places for bog plants; and the fact that this sounds simple and obvious shows how completely we have accepted his tenets. For to him a rock garden was no mere display of rocks. Better they be buried underground (at a downward inward slant to carry moisture to thirsty roots) than stuck up in Almond Pudding or Plum Bun fashion. He was always eager to pass on his knowledge of a plant's terrain so that, transplanted into an English garden, his treasures might find a natural home.

He followed the family tradition by going to Balliol College, Oxford, there soon finding a congenial friend in the gardening don, the Rev Henry Jardine Bidder. Together they laid out the famous rock garden on the edge of the great lawn at St John's. He celebrated his graduation with a journey round the world, starting with a visit to the Continent in 1903.

From this trip, among other plants he sent home were two

which added fresh glories to the rock garden. Farrer is credited with three outstanding saxifrages. A 1903 discovery was *Saxifraga aizoon rex*, one of the finest sandstone types. He found it on the upper moraine of the Dossenhorn: crowded neat masses of stiff expanding rosettes, each richly beaded with silver and carrying on its 8–10in mahogany-red stems large cream-white flowers. It became a free grower and flowerer. Then under the slopes of the Vorder Wellhorn he came across a very fine form of *Campanula bellardii*. It was dwarf but with enormous flowers of delicate silvery blue 'like a fine cloud at night with the moon behind it', as Farrer characteristically described its diaphanous pallor. He named it 'Miranda' after his cousin and predicted that it would be one of the greatest of our rock-garden plants. Carefully packed and despatched to England, with special instructions to the Ingleborough head gardener for dealing with it, the campanula had disappeared. Then, five years later, it pushed up leaves and broke into blossom, and grew and grew 'with the rapidity of gout-weed'.

Then began his real travels, his visits to China and Japan resulting in a fascinating book, *The Garden of Asia*, which ran into a second impression, and a lecture to the Royal Horticultural Society on Japanese plants and gardens. It was an astonishment to his audience when he told them that English sentiment was apt to assume that the Japanese loved all flowers equally, and that while the iris, cherry, peach, bamboo, magnolia, wistaria, azalea, camellia, lotus, plum and pine were among the elect, the rose and the lily were unrefined flowers according to Japanese artistic laws, and, as such, more or less beyond the pale of horticultural tolerance. Even the favoured plants, Farrer found, were rarely allowed to appear in the garden proper, this being a miniature landscape of architectural rather than cultural art, where symbolism governed the correct placing of every rock and stone. The favoured plants were grown in beds beyond the landscape, so as not to interfere with its proportions. For all that, many Japanese wild plants were worth growing in English gardens.

He instanced *Rhododendron dilatatum* which, despite its astonishing beauty, had not yet come into general culture. An alpine species with campanulate flowers of brilliant soft rose, Farrer said of it: 'If this plant can ever be introduced into cultivation it would soon rank among the most beautiful of shrubs.' (*R. dilatatum* is now classed as *R. reticulatum* var. *pentandrum*.)

The Far East cast its spell on him, and in 1907 he went to Ceylon where he became a Buddhist. It was no passing whim: he retained a real and deep feeling for his faith, though never taking himself too seriously. Sir Osbert Sitwell, who was Farrer's second cousin, relates in his *Noble Essences* the amusing story of how Reginald went to see a Living Buddha residing in Ceylon's interior, who gave him some useful advice on the subject of dealing with a man-eating tiger.

He was back in the Far East in 1914, meantime filling the intervening years with much activity: writing, gardening, and collecting in the European mountains with kindred souls he met at the shows of the Royal Horticultural Society. *My Rock Garden*, his first gardening book, was published in 1907, in which year he also published two novels, a form of writing in which (like his attempts to enter politics) he was never really successful. He also extended the Ingleborough rock garden by hewing a path along the cliff face, and established his own Craven Nursery, propagating plants from Ingleborough and sending out a first catalogue. The next year was prolific with *Alpines and Bog Plants*, *In Old Ceylon*, a play and a novel.

The book on alpines gave descriptions of Airolo in the Lepontine Alps, the first place on the southern side of the St Gothard Tunnel. This and Piora, 2,000ft higher in the mountains, were famed for flowers, especially in June when the alpine meadows were like the gayest of gardens and on the heights the little soldanellas were lifting their purple bells above the snow. E. A. Bowles, a great gardener who was to become Farrer's closest friend, went there in 1909 on the recommendation of another great gardener, Canon Henry

Nicholson Ellacombe of Bitton in Gloucestershire. A sufferer from hay fever and finding that above 3,000ft he was clear of his trouble, Bowles went to the Alps every year and collected plants for his own rock garden. So when he and Farrer first met at the RHS in May 1910 they found a common interest. Farrer told him that he was off in June for a 'cheap little humble trip of six weeks or so round the Graian, Cottian and Maritime Alps'. Bowles was going to the Savoy, to scour the hills around Modane on the French-Italian frontier. They arranged to meet at Mont Cenis.

To go collecting with Reginald Farrer was an education, and usually each climb was to find one particular thing. On this occasion the object of their search was that rare and precious cousin of the primrose, *Cortusa matthiola*, the Alpine Bells. Farrer knew to look for it among alders, and there he found its rosy-magenta flowers hanging in a loose shower 'like the falling stars of a rocket'. He was a fearless and tireless climber. Clarence Elliott, himself an experienced collector in many lands, recalled one tremendous month he spent with Farrer in the Alps. It started with thirteen hours of hot and tedious transcontinental rail travel, five hours' sleep, another sixteen hours' travel by rail and carriage, six hours' sleep, and then an early-morning start for an expedition of sixteen hours' severe climb and scramble – to get one plant, *Daphne rupestris*. There was a grilling day by steamboat from end to end of Lake Garda, followed by an execrable rail journey and finally a night drive in a tiny landau through floods of icy rain in a thunderstorm to Ferrara, which they reached at midnight. Their terrible dinner was one of sardines, Marie biscuits and *crème de menthe*. Yet Farrer insisted, during the last and worst hours of that pitiless night drive, that all conversation should be carried on in verse! 'He was always good company, always stimulating,' was Elliott's unbiased comment.

Farrer wrote up his 1910 trip in *Among the Hills*, which was published the following year. He dedicated it to Augustus Bowles, the leading authority on crocuses, in these words:

Ave Crocorum Omnium Rex Imperator Paterculus Augustus, 'Hail to thee, of all crocuses King and Emperor, Little Father Augustus!' The 'Little Father' was a version of their nicknames for each other – Bowles, fifteen years older, being Farrer's 'Nephew', Farrer, Bowles's 'Uncle', and in these terms they addressed each other in a series of letters exchanged till Farrer's last days, meanwhile plant hunting together again in 1911, 1912 and 1913.

It was these forays among the European Alps that made Farrer a plant hunter. Always, arriving at a new place, he would question the local guides as to where certain plants might be found, and previously would brief himself with all the information he could pick up. Typical of this was the postcard he sent to Bowles in September 1912 from Idria, writing:

> These are the wilds of Slavonia where alone in a tiny district here and there lives Prim. carniolica. Now, does my memory cheat me in thinking it was some friend of yours who had seen Omph[alogramma] luciliae near Smyrna? If not, do please find out exactly where, & how one goes to it and send me the result c/o Cook, 107 Rue Cabristan, Constantinople, on the chance of my going there.

Most importantly Farrer had an eye for a plant, for a new form or a new flower-colour.

Arthur Churchill Bartholomew, the dahlia grower, and Farrer's brother Sidney were with them in 1911. They made their base at Modane, and it is evident from Bowles's diary that Farrer was the alpine expert. On finding drifts and sheets of thousands of *Anemone alpina*, 'R.F. pointed out that they have a dioecious tendency'; and when, that same day, climbing in the mountains, 'the way home seemed so long and unfamiliar that B & I thought we were lost, R.F. knew what he was about & we got home in the end'. Saxifrages, primulas and anemones were their quarries, with gentians ('R.F. found a nearly white one'), campanulas and such other alpines as drabas. Their harvest was packed into the large biscuit tins Farrer had found ideal for transporting plants. Greatest of their treasures was *Eritrichium nanum*, the King of the Alps. It was '*the* typical high-alpine, only to be seen with climbing and effort', as Farrer pointed out.

It is the motto of the mountaineer, and the crown of achievement for the walker in the Alps, who will have trudged over leagues of Flannel-flower [thus scornfully did he dismiss the Edelweiss as a true alpine] before once he captured sight of the King of the Alps, set in blobs of sky across the face of some dark cliff, or on some sunny slope of the highest ridges making blots of fallen heaven among the scanty herbage of the hill.

The Farrers and Bowles found it on the Col du Clapier after a long stodge up over the snow in a bitterly cold wind with sleet falling. But when they reached the bare rock-tops and saw Eritrichium's silvery tufts, 'we minded nothing'. A plant almost impossible to acclimatise, Farrer gave advice on how it might survive away from its own inhospitable ridges, but recommended that the King of the Alps be adored, not touched. 'To take him from his native premises seems murder as clear as to bruise a butterfly in our hands.'

In February 1912 Farrer was writing to lure his 'nephew' to the Dolomites. They would 'whirl out straight to Vienna by the great Express and drive south to the Hochschneeberg, where Prim. Clusiana, Auricula, minima, intermedia, will be in acres of glory'. Farrer wanted to be '*quite* certain there is no hybrid Clusiana X auricula'. It would be a lightning fourteen days, with the '*divine* motor trip over the Karer Pass, the Pordoi Pass, the Falzarego Pass, through the very heart of all the Dolomites'. They would go in June.

Before then, from 22 to 30 May, the Royal International Horticultural Exhibition was staged in the grounds of the Chelsea Royal Hospital. Farrer was a vice-president of the committee and one of the judges of the alpine section. His own Craven Nursery won the first prize for alpine plants displayed in a space not exceeding 100sq ft.

It was the first horticultural exhibition of an international character since 1866, and by far the most important ever held in Britain. To Reginald Cory, a wealthy industrialist who became a benefactor of the Royal Horticultural Society, it seemed deplorable that the exhibition should survive only as a memory, and with the help of R. Hooper Pearson, editor of the *Gardeners Chronicle*, he compiled an illustrated record. The first article in the huge book, on 'Rock Gardens and Garden Design', was by Reginald Farrer. It was an outstanding survey of garden design through the ages, and of course when he came to discuss the planning and planting of a rock garden it was in the mood of Farrer's best rhetoric. But what he wrote was truth. It was also sheer common sense. 'Most unbearable of all things is the too common rock-garden, chucked together blindly, as if any chaos were sufficient, or built of fried cement, or some artificial concoction baked into stalactites. Why do so many people think that the rock garden is the happy home of anarchy and unguided personal whim?' Wildness without law was chaos, he declared, but 'composed with regard to rhythm it is the loveliest example of chained force that art can offer.' In asking Reginald Farrer to write the article, Cory and Hooper Pearson were recognising him as the leader in alpine gardening.

Farrer commemorated the trip to the Dolomites in his book of that name, sub-titled *King Laurin's Garden*. His very first sentence was an enchantment. 'King Laurin's Garden is a land of magic,' he wrote, 'enclosed by peaks like frozen flames.' The strange pink mountains thrusting their jagged pinnacles above a sea of hills fascinated him beyond all other ranges. They were a paradise of flowers, teaching Farrer fresh lessons in the ecology of alpine plants and raising him to heights of ecstasy in beholding them among the splendours of King Laurin's domain. He saw again *Eritrichium nanum* on the crest of a ridge, 'tuffets of silver fluff mosaicked with their mass of azure Forget-me-Nots', and on a rocky crest of the Padon Chain a snow-white King of the Alps 'with flowers half again as big as usual and variegated leaves with a golden margin'. To reach it, crawling gingerly across a rock-face, he had to summon all his courage. But somewhere, on some blessed ridge or cliff, he had always felt, there must be a snow-white eritrichium. He came upon primulas growing by the acre, as thick as bluebells in an English wood. The fragrant *Primula longiflora*, rare in Switzerland, was abundant on the grassy lawns of the Forcella Lungieres and the Schlern, sending up its long bugle stars of dim rose above shimmering pink carpets of *Primula minima*. In his *English Rock Garden* he had much to say to his gardener readers about primulas and their hybrids and how to cultivate them successfully.

In June 1913 Farrer and Bowles again went plant hunting together, this time joined by A. Clutton Brock who proved himself no climber. Starting from San Dalmazzo they ranged round the Alpes Maritimes, once more in search of primulas but adding pinguiculas, dianthus, campanulas and androsaces. A prize was *Primula cottia*, discovered at a group of rocks near Bobbio, a new station for this very rare species. Farrer was generous. He and Bowles went up the Col de la Croix where they were astounded to find undoubted hybrids of two species of primulas, *marginata* and *viscosa*, ranging from red-purple to blue. The bluest of all fell three times to Bowles's trowel, and three times he offered the crowns to Farrer who 'nobly refused' them. This striking form Farrer christened *P. crucis* Blue Bowl, thus perpetrating the sort of pun he was fond of inventing.

But by then Farrer's eyes were set on the Far East. In April he had attended the Primula Conference and lectured on European primulas. There he was dazzled by a brand-new species hailed the previous month at the RHS Fortnightly Show as the most distinct hardy plant novelty of the year. Not surprisingly it had won a First Class Certificate. Its foot-long stems broke out into a rocket-spray of large clear lilac stars, the exquisite complement of its ash-grey leaves which were so thickly powdery that 'the whole tuft looks as though it has lived all its years beside a popular motoring road', as Farrer later wrote of it. It was named *Primula purdomii* after its discoverer, William Purdom, home from a successful expedition for Veitch and the Arnold Arboretum. Purdom had found it between 10,000 and 11,000ft up in the high grasslands of West Kansu.

The primula set Farrer thinking. What of the Kansu-Tibetan border? E. H. Wilson had worked the provinces of the southern border, and George Forrest and Frank Kingdon Ward were still there. But the Kansu March remained virgin territory. Two great Russian explorers, Potanin and Przewalski, had traversed the region, but only to get dried specimens. Botanically they had left it unexplored, while the alpine chain up through the Tibetan border remained untrodden. In this remote northerly province, Farrer thought, might be found a flora more resistant and useful in the British climate than the softer plants of Yunnan and Szechuan.

He sought an introduction to Purdom and knew from the first moment of their meeting that his instinct was sound. Purdom, when asked whether – for no more exciting prospect than his expenses – he would be willing to share and direct a perfect stranger's venture towards the Tibetan March, said he would. They left England on 7 February 1914, having planned the Kansu expedition on a generous time-scale. First they would deal with the ranges on the southern border and then, after wintering somewhere midway, move north in 1915 for a season's exploration in the alps above Si-ning.

The scheme, despite tremendous difficulties, was achieved with perfect success and with results of a richness that surpassed Farrer's every hope.

The new trans-Siberian railway, completed ten years before, took them to Peking where they engaged three servants. One, Mafu, had previously been employed by Purdom, and though the ugliest man Farrer had ever seen ('Imagine a bandylegged rhomboidal gorilla, gap-toothed and rubicund, capable of blossoming into a demoniac fury of yells and leaps and howls that might well afright a fiend') he was well used to rough-and-ready travelling. The second was Go-go, his brother, fresh from his Shansi village and almost paralysed with terror at seeing his first European. The third, an unknown quantity, though guaranteed by Mafu, was cook. On 5 March they left the Imperial city by train for Honan and the railway terminus at Mien-chi-Hsien. And here their troubles began. Insurrection was seething on the Kansu-Tibetan border whither they were bound, and no contractor would hire out mules lest they fall into the hands of White Wolf and his brigand army. After much bargaining they hired riding ponies and three carts to carry their baggage (which included a weighty supply of silver ingots to pay their way for two years).

Three days out of Tsin Chow in South Kansu they made their first find. The weather was dark and cheerless. They were winding along a dull ascent between looming mountains when, among the scrub and coppice that grew down to the track they were following, they came on a shrub mantled in white and pink. The single bush became many as they went on, leaving them in no doubt that here it was genuinely indigenous. All over North China it was probably the best-loved and most familiar of garden plants. Now, as Farrer wrote in *On the Eaves of the World*: 'April 16 is an important date in botanical history, as marking the first discovery of *Viburnum fragrans* as a wild plant.' It has become probably the best-loved and most familiar of our own garden shrubs. 'In cultivation,' Farrer wrote, 'I dare to foretell it will give no trouble ... either as to aspect or treatment in any nutritious loam. May it soon yield us the secular glory of the superb bushes that it makes in the yards of the Prince of Jo-ni or the great Green Temple at Lanchow ... ' It was in the gardens of the Prince of Jo-ni that he tried to get some seeds. Alas, His Highness would not part with them. In fact: 'The Prince ate all his, but this was got elsewhere,' as he explained in the RHS *Journal*.

They had seen a sturdy glossy little daphne, and as the viburnum ceased it now took over, populating the rocky gorges with crowded heads of fragrant pale pink flowers. This was his *Daphne tangutica*.

They were bound for Kiai Chow, and traversing the high open downs great was their delight to find a hillside blue with clumped masses of *Iris ensata*. Farrer gave it the name Hyacinthina. The next discovery was at the village of Fu-erh-Gai, the Street of Happy Sons, where on an evening walk through a copse Farrer found *Paeonia moutan* (*suffruticosa*) growing as a wild plant. Its enormous single blossoms on tall stems were waved and crimped. The pure white of its petals had featherings of deepest maroon radiating from a boss of golden fluff. As with the viburnum, the native home of this peony had long been a botanical mystery. In 1911 Purdom had discovered the red form. Farrer's form, of the purest white, became a welcome addition to English gardens. Two days later they reached Kiai Chow on the Hei-shui-jang or Blackwater River. They were now at the start of their real journey, striking due westward up towards Tibet.

Luck was with them. By following a route southward, then climbing west to Wen-hsien, they just escaped White Wolf and his hordes who came charging up the Blackwater. But entering Tibetan territory in the Sha-Tan Alps, the lamas became unfriendly when Farrer innocently violated a local taboo. He narrowly escaped being murdered and withdrew north to the Chinese village of Ga-hoba, there waiting for a few days before journeying west again.

Going round the heel of Kansu they emerged from the bottom of a gorge on to a wide desert of boulders. There among the blocks of stone flaunted a buddleia with huge foliage of grey flannel, the scent from its golden-eyed lavender stars reminding Farrer of a delicious raspberry ice! It now grows in our gardens in sheltered places facing the sun.

Farrer always gave charming names to his primroses: the Pretty Primula, the Oriad, Clusterbeauty, the Welcome Primula. Now he found the Rock Nymph (*Primula scopulorum*) glinting rosy-purple among the damp moss wads of a precipice. Then came another primula, *loczii*, which he found in a wood. It had rose-pink heads above rosettes that sent out runners like 'some questing vegetable octopus'.

Mafu and Mee the cook had ridden on ahead to secure lodgings at Chago, to which there were two tracks, one a steep and stony climb that wound round the hillside, the other smooth and pleasant through fields of young corn. Purdom chose the high course, Go-go and Farrer the low track – from which they were chased by the howls and hoots of the villagers, for this path, though open to pedestrians, was forbidden to ponies. In a sore mood after a wearying day Farrer returned to the high path, and there discovered the charming little honeysuckle which was given his name, *Lonicera farreri*. Showers of dropping rosy trumpets grew all along its flattened sprays of tiny leaves.

Then came the Satanee Alps and *Primula silvia* whose flowers glowed like rubies above soft green crumpled foliage. Sadly, the lovely Dryad did not survive in cultivation. The next treasure was a new rhododendron, also named after Farrer. It was growing 14ft tall and was laden with trusses of large and most lovely shell-pink flowers. Farrer guessed that it would never earn the applause of the fanciers who ruled that show rhododendrons must, as he put it, 'wear their flowers in a dense fat cone like a giant artichoke', and sadly this was their verdict. But *Rhododendron reginaldi* pleased its discoverer, who deemed that the loosely borne pearl-pink trumpets and oval emerald blades at each spray's end made it one of the loveliest of its kin.

Along the Himalayan borders and reaching into the southern marches of Tibet, there lived a strange race of primulas which are now considered not to be primulas at all. Indeed they more resemble small gloxinias or gigantic pinguiculas. Before the leaves fully unfold, the plant unfurls a solitary huge flower of rich purple. In a gully loud with the noise of a waterfall Farrer suddenly saw it, a flare of purple at his feet. The upper 'petals' lay flat back like an angry cat's ears, the lower ones pushed forward like an angry child's pout. Farrer sent home the paradoxical plant as *Primula viola-grandis*. It is now named *Omphalogramma farreri*. 'A glorious species – most precious,' he extolled it.

In an alpine coppice he found *Berberis dasystachya*, a big bush with arching sprays hanging out tails of yellow blossoms like tiny roses and scented as sweetly as a lily. Bad news now reached them. The Wolves had been seen at a village just over the Red Range, and more were reported to be coming across Chagola on horseback, which would cut off the way to Saku. After preparing for a siege Farrer decided to retreat to Ga-hoba. He dug primulas as he went, and they reached safety at Mö-Ping, a large village on the other side of the Red Range at the head of a gigantic gorge. Between the village and the gorge was a riot of beauty: a tangled blaze of snowy deutzia, golden forsythia, honeysuckles and roses in plumy and cloudy weights of snow and sheaves of softest pink. No shrubbery, even the richest, had ever shown Farrer such a prodigal wild surf of loveliness. Descending the gorge they followed it until the valley widened out into a smiling glen. From Nain Dzai they looked across to the enormous mass of Thundercrown which was to give them a harvest. The loess cliffs about Nain Dzai revealed a new buddleia whose long streaming cascades of leaves resembled a weeping willow when it was not in flower, 'and a sheer waterfall of soft purple when it is'. *Buddleia alternifolia,* a most lovely plant, was to prove hardy in English gardens. It won the Award of Merit and the Award of Garden Merit.

The anemone is the one alpine plant of importance in our gardens which is found in an unbroken chain of distribution right across the world. On the approaches to Thundercrown, Farrer saw far up on a cliff a shimmering whiteness which, when he came nearer, resolved into a wide drift of magnificent fluffy anemones flopping their heads of big white blossoms from every ledge. It was named *Anemone farreri.* Soon after, coming abruptly to the end of their climb, they found themselves on the verge of a deep precipice, Thundercrown facing them across a vast and tumbled chaos of wooded gorges far away beneath them. But before they could storm its heights they had to cool their heels at Siku, so far untouched by the Wolves but now under imminent threat. In the interval of waiting Farrer and Purdom scoured the great gorges behind the town, finding two prizes: the Harebell Poppy (*Meconopsis quintuplinerva*), first discovered in 1877, and a stray specimen of the Celestial Poppy

(*M. prattii*) which was new. It made a superb pyramid of azure-blue flowers.

It was not until 20 June that, with the countryside quiet again, they moved their camp on to Thundercrown. Three days later, up 12,000ft, Farrer wrote a long letter to his 'nephew', E. A. Bowles.

> We have been winding right through the rebellion for the last 2 months, & it is a perfect miracle, that, with all our caravan & all our great square boxes filled with bullion, we should hitherto have *just* passed ahead of the rebels by two or three days, through towns subsequently laid waste by fire & sword & finally, after the most urgent perils of all, have drifted into the one little city which the marauders had not thought it worth their while to diverge against.

Bowles, A. K. Bulley and others, and the Royal Horticultural Society, had contributed funds for the expedition, and Farrer thought that the RHS 'need not regret its venture – & I hope you will make it understand through what a welter of hair-breadth perils its ends are being sought! There will soon be no skin left on my teeth to escape by.' Even now, the grassy slope on which he lay was

> jewelled with a lovely mauve Iris, a clustered sweet wee pink lonicera, a wee golden trollius [sent home as *T. pumilis perfectissimus*], a great violet nivalis-Primula, a pale yellow Fritilaria, Meconopsis quintuplinervia (a sound *perennial*!), M. integrifolia & a third little M. (new I think, but near Delavayi) with many petalled flowers of blue silk, as perky & upborne as a sunflower's. And of other treasures there is Prim. flava, a *lovely* lavender-blue powder-stemmed nivalis cousin, a little queer, standing between sibirica & longiflora, only found on the mud of the mountain track (& there as thick as groundsel coming up) a dainty lilac rock-species carrying one's heart back to P. hirsuta on the Grigna, & a beautiful woodland species, in all its habits suggesting a strange lilac little Polyanthus. So you see, in Prim. alone we have already managed not to do so badly.

He had also found the noble *Rodgersia aesculifolia* of huge bronze leaves and towering plumes.

Already they had achieved the topmost saddle of the mountain where, as on the fearful stone desolation, the flora was disappointingly poor. But the upper screes of Thundercrown had yielded a new aster of gold-eyed purple daisies (*Aster kansuensis*), and on the way up they had found a delightful annual incarvillea with small lemon-yellow flowers (*I. variabilis* var. *Przewalski*), and one of the finest deutzias ever to come into cultivation. It whitened the coppiced slopes with a surf of snow and was named *Deutzia albida*. Now, Farrer wrote, having sucked all the sweets of the mountain, they would descend again as soon as possible and head for what was left of ravaged Minchow.

Their way led through the gloomy splendours of the Nan-Hor gorges, then over scrubby downs into open country. The hills began again and the Tibetan androsace appeared in mats along by the path. Up the steeps they climbed, the flora becoming more and more alpine. On the crest and over it, the show of flowers on the northern face was dazzling. Another new aster greeted them, the single-flowered lavender *limitaneus* – Middle Bear, Farrer called it: he was to find Big Bear later on. Edelweiss and Grass of Parnassus grew in jungles and sheets of silver and white, and in a rich moist bank the Harebell Poppy formed huge dense tussocks with as many as fifty big lavender butterfly-flowers hovering over each clump. After a gruelling trudge over stony stretches and up river valleys they reached Min-jô, and finding that the Wolves had smashed the bridge across the Tao River into China they continued along the Tibetan side until they were able to cross by a rope ferry. On reaching the royal city of Jo-ni it was to find it in a state of fear and flight, and it was only with the Prince's permission that they set up camp on the alps.

They managed to make an excursion up the Mirgo Valley, where Farrer came upon Big Bear, the aster that later bore his name. One of the plants about which he was most enthusiastic, for its narrow violet florets and great orange eye, it is now common in cultivation. Other spoils were *Geranium pylzowianum*, like a very frail *G. sanguineum* but with bigger flowers of a clean soft pink; *Leontopodium haplophylloides,* the lemon-scented edelweiss, considered one of the best of Farrer's smaller introductions; and in a deep limestone gorge *Syringa potaninii* of large panicles of pure white scented flowers, which proved a first class garden plant and won an RHS Award of Merit. There was also a bush potentilla 'of indescribable beauty in masses of brightest gold to snowiest white, with every intermediate shade of cream and butter and canary and moonlight saffron'. This was one of Farrer's finest of all introductions, *Potentilla fruticosa,* to be found today in almost every garden.

On 27 July they left Jo-ni and crossed again into Tibet, following the track up to Bao-u-go, and as they climbed the flowers and vegetation became more and more luxuriant. Coming to a rickety bridge they had to cross, Farrer's pony took fright midway and backed through the handrails, plunging himself and his rider into the boiling ice-grey torrent below. To swim was impossible. The current carried Farrer rapidly downstream – and upright because of the weight of his heavy mountain boots, so that, as he wrote: 'I could study the Primulas in their crannies as they fled blandly by.' It was fortunate that the tumbling waters soon spread themselves into a long wide shallow, otherwise he would have been drowned. He dried off in a Tibetan farmhouse and next day set off for the Stone Mountain.

Here new treasures awaited him, in a wild land of crags and high alpine meadows filled with his little purple asters, pale golden saxifrages, gentians in masses of softest water-blue, with galaxies of the silver stars of edelweiss and the cerulean fluffballs of the bluebell garlic. Suddenly in the chorus of colour he caught a new note, *Meconopsis psilonomma,* the Lonely Poppy, bearing on its solitary stem a single purple flower. It throve in cultivation until 1917 and then was lost, and Farrer never discovered it again. Now attaining the crest of the Red Ridge he looked down to a hoar-frosted carpet of the Silver Geranium, another plant that was to bear his name. On the same day a last discovery was *Androsace mucronifolia* making living snow-patches in emerald turf.

They returned to Jo-ni to make their plans for the autumn, for seed-time was almost upon them. It was decided that Purdom should harvest the Jo-ni ranges, while Farrer hurried off to Siku to glean the harvest there. As they sat talking that night in 1914, a missionary they knew burst in with the news that France and Germany were at war.

Arriving back at Siku felt so much like coming home that Farrer lost no time in setting off on his first expedition, and while collecting seeds he found more plants new to him. Among them were *Buddleia variabilis* (*davidii*) which proved a fine garden plant; *Lilium duchartrei*, the Marble Martagon, a glory of orange and black, and on a second and longer expedition *Gentiana hexaphylla*, dazzlingly beautiful with long trumpets of clear pale blue. In cultivation it grows best in northern gardens.

When the season's plants and seeds went back to England, some of them arrived at Myddelton House, Enfield, where Farrer's 'nephew' dealt with them skilfully. *Rosa multibracteata* duly pushed up but proved poor and straggly. But among the seedlings was a stray, which received the name *Rosa farreri* var. *persetosa*. It was the Threepenny-bit Rose, of exquisite single pink flowers.

Uncle wrote to Nephew in November from Lanchow in Kansu. He was resting after the *Sturm und Drang* of seed collecting. But the haul was immense and of the greatest value, 'presenting all the best of Potanin's herbarium stuff, as I hope next year will present Przewalsky's. Two *new* Poppies, please you, 2 glorious Androsaces, a Delphinium like a huge violet butterfly hovering close over the high scree (D. tanguticum?), Primulas, *25 species* ... & all the rest to match!!'

The next season, 1915, opened with the Chinese New Year at Lanchow, lasting a noisy fortnight, but it was not until the end of March when Bill Purdom returned from Tibet, laden with treasures, that they set out again. Seven months' work lay ahead of them in a journey across the Gadjur mountains and the Da-tung alps in a circle back to Lanchow, then striking south-east through the Min-shan mountains.

The earth was waking, and at Sining-Fu Farrer found his first flower of the year, the dainty tufted *Viola patrinii*, 'like golden-bodied butterflies of a lucent blue lavender'. He met again his *Iris ensata*, and his frosty edelweiss which he foresaw as a wonderful plant grown with 'the purple chalices of Crocus speciosus … poking through its silver floor'. Up 11,000ft in the Wolfstone Valley he and Purdom hired a house as their base for six months, at half-a-crown for the duration, using its back yard as a nursery for their plants. Though the hills and valleys were carpeted with spring flowers, new ones were hard to find. But on every cliff clung *Lloydia alpina*. Farrer called it the Fairy Bells and wrote that some might not find the little plant 'striking' enough for their taste, but that 'to me its phantasmal bells have a quite special charm, as they swing out and float and hover, like glassy bubbles, along the stern dark lines of the cliffs, the thinly-touched streak of mahogany down the outside of each silvery segment contributing a curious look of elfin transparency to its already elfin grace'.

It was still too early for the heights and they moved down to the lowlands for a few weeks. 'And now turned up unbeknownest in Mafu's anthropoid fist, an *Isopyrum* that simply sent *grandiflorum* supperless to bed,' Farrer exulted. It was 'like a much handsomer sea-blue maidenhair, from out of which came dancing great silken blossoms of sheeny lavender purple.'

Back at Wolvesden the alpine lawns now revealed something new every day. Once they were caught in a snowstorm and as they stopped to rest, Farrer perceived a thin shoot straggling among the moss. 'Hello, Bill,' he said, 'here will be a gentian one of these days,' and thought no more about it until they returned to Wolvesden at the end of August for the seed harvest. The beautiful *Gentiana farreri*, now listed in every alpine nurseryman's catalogue, has established itself as a living memorial to its discoverer.

Farrer's greatest joy was to find a new primula, and on the last 50ft of Crest Royal's summit there gleamed 'one solitary spark of rosy flame on the dark desolation'. *Primula reginella* (now *P. fasciculata*) was a real jewel. On the broad stretch of moor they came upon variants of the meconopsis, shifting through rosy and amethystine tones, some azure-blue, with rare white ones pure as snowflakes. In his book *The Rainbow Bridge* Farrer urged his readers to raise seed of the Harebell Poppy, and go on raising it, 'on the chance of one day blooming a drop of mortal rainbow'.

The Russians Potanin and Przewalski had left misleadingly rosy accounts of the spoils to be found in the granite range they were now exploring, and Farrer had the feeling that they were too far north. Limestone alone (as always) had yielded them the few chief treasures of the year. Now there only remained the dolomite precipices opposite Kerauno and its pass. But here again there was nothing new. Facing failure they decided to return to Wolvesden and separate, Purdom to go off to the Koko-nor while Farrer collected the harvest of Da-tung. It was a bitter disappointment when Purdom's plants turned out to be much the same as they had already collected. Farrer, patrolling what he called the Jardin, realised that all his expeditions in the Da-tung alps had been wasted. For here in this stretch of a quarter of a mile long by a few hundred yards deep, occurred every high alpine flower he had found in the whole course of the season's arduous and unrewarding expeditions, with the solitary exception of *Primula urticifolia*, the Pretty Primula which, too, was a disappointment. For it did not survive in cultivation. Sick with failure he retraced his steps to Wolvesden, and it was then, as he came back over the Crest Royal, he found his gentian in flower, a marvel of luminous loveliness. It literally burned in the alpine turf like an incandescent turquoise.

There was no question of waiting for seeds. He dug up living plants. And the steam heat of the trans-Siberian railway killed them all. Home in England, the war submerged him in work, and the beautiful gentian ceased to exist except as a haunting memory. Then in August 1916 a little packet reached him from Edinburgh's Botanic Garden. Would he give the history of the enclosed gentian? It had grown from seed collected on Thundercrown.

It was his lost gentian.

He had come home to acclaim. Even before he left Peking a letter arrived from Sir Isaac Bayley Balfour, Keeper of Edinburgh's Garden. It was written 'most radiantly', as Farrer told his Nephew and said that 'quite apart from the fine proportion of *new* new species I have nobbled a notable number of fine things hitherto only known in herbaria.'

He thought more kindly now of 'all that fairyland' of the Da-tung, and confessed to Bowles: 'I do so hate being at the end of it all: do you think I shall find anyone to help in another such expedition? I do feel now that we have really been proved worth our salt.'

It was not until 1919 that he set foot again in Asia, when he found a plant-hunting companion in E. H. M. Cox who was to become a connoisseur of rhododendrons. Their goal was Upper Burma, their quarries, of course, the alpine plants Farrer loved beyond all others. But when they got there it was to find that the Burmese hills did not breed the kind of alpines that give any return for care or kindness at the hands of the gardener, as Euan Cox put it. The only saxifrages were of the Hirculus section, difficult species needing bog or damp scree conditions. The primulas were of groups proving unfriendly in alien soil, and this applied to the vast majority of the other alpines. Not that there were very many of them. Woody plants such as low-growing berberis, bamboo, creeping willow and stunted rowans monopolised most of the growing-space above the tree-line, so that cremanthodiums had to push up through thickets of dwarf rhododendrons, primulas content themselves with mossy boulders, omphalogrammas be satisfied with a foot or two of freedom among bamboos. The only gentian worth looking at was relegated to stone slides and gravel beds. No wonder that Farrer was overwhelmed by the weight of the possessive ligneous plants and longed for heights where his beloved alpines were not crowded out of existence.

Of the actual alpine plants Farrer found on this expedition, Cox reckoned that only sixteen were good enough to be called suitable for the rock garden, and of these few survive in cultivation. Exceptions include *Primula sonchifolia*, now well established, which so kindled the heart of its finder that he first named it *gratissima*! It has rich wide lavender-blue flowers delicately fringed all round the lobes. The dainty little *Gaultheria trichophylla*, producing an astonishing crop of lapis-lazuli berries, won an RHS Award of Merit. Also successful when sown straight into the garden was *Nomocharis farreri*, whose generic name means the grace or charm of the pasture. Related to the fritillary and lily its soft pink petals are freckled inside with red spots. *Omphalogramma farreri* survived at Edinburgh. In Farrer's words it was 'a real glory with enormous fringed flowers of violet-purple'. It is the most striking of all aralias. There remained three dwarf rhododendrons: *aperantum*, of which Cox said: 'I wonder if gardeners realise what a treasure it is going to be'; *calostrotum* with bronzy foliage and rosy or pale pink saucer flowers, which has proved one of the best of all dwarf rhododendrons; and *myrtilloides* with bell-shaped waxy plum-purple flowers.

But if the alpines disappointed Farrer, there were rich compensations in other plants, so that when he wrote to his Nephew in December 1919 he was able to sum up the year's work as 'a season that seems to me almost uncannily triumphant.'

Among woody plants was a 'particularly pink and prodigal' form of *Luculia pinceana*. 'Far above praise,' Farrer rated it. 'Few shrubs are so perfectly beautiful and in every way desirable.' Semi-evergreen and with delicately scented flowers in bloom from May to September it throve in the gardens at Exbury and Bodnant, and won an Award of Merit. Three trees were outstanding. *Michelia doltsopa* (found in 1848 on Tonglu by Joseph Hooker but, if introduced, did not survive), in magnificence second only to Hooker's *Magnolia campbellii*, is small to medium-size and semi-evergreen in the south-west of England, with big ivory-white flowers so densely covering it in April that the leaves are not visible. *Magnolia nitida*, one of the tallest growing of its kind and distinguished for its grey bole and the metallic lustre of its young growths, has an abundance of fragrant ivory-cream flowers. Farrer found it on Hpimaw, up 8,000ft, on the fringes of a forest. Though subjected to bitter winters in its homeland, in Britain it must be grown in a sheltered place and in a mild locality such as Cornwall. Then there was *Juniperus coxii*, one of Farrer's best introductions. 'A remarkably lovely graceful weeping grey-green "Cypress",' he described it. He and Cox found it 10,000ft up while exploring the Chimili Valley near the Yunnan border. This is still generally, and mistakenly, called the Coffin Tree. The name arose from a misunderstanding. Almost every day Farrer and Cox used to see coolies or mules laden with huge 9-ft planks for coffins, of a very fragrant wood. They never found the tree from which they were cut, but did come across a burnt-out shell, so large that six people could stand inside. By an odd coincidence it was surrounded by some young trees of *Juniperus recurva* var. *coxii* (*J. coxii*), and quite wrongly they assumed them to be seedlings of this giant tree. It was not until twenty years later that Kingdon Ward established that the coffin planks came from *Taiwania cryptomerioides*, the tree Wilson found in Formosa on his last trip to the Far East.

No Farrer plant-hunts would be complete without primulas. The 1919 expedition furnished two: *Primula limnoica* of lavender-blue flowers, and *P. burmanica* of foot-long leaves and reddish-purple flowers with a yellow eye. He found others but unfortunately they did not thrive. This was not due to the quality of the plants but to the difference in climatic conditions between Upper Burma and the British Isles. Where almost similar conditions could be given them, some highly successful Farrer plants found a home in the gardens at Logan on the Mull of Galloway where even tropical plants flourish in the mild air of the Gulf Stream. So there the superb *Lobelia pyramidalis*, of long weeping boughs and narrow pale purple flowers, was able to flourish, with Farrer's *Lilium ochraceum* ('a lily without a fault'), and *Ilex odorata*, a shrub with long drooping sprays set with beautiful turquoise berries. *Rhododendron supranubium* also proved hardy at Logan and at the famous garden at Exbury in Hampshire, a small bush with very large lovely flowers of pure rose flushed with white and intensely fragrant. Another fairly tender rhododendron was *kyawi*, scarlet-crimson and one of the richest coloured of all rhododendrons.

Hardy were *Rhododendron neriiflorum* var. *phoenicodum*, a bush of 6–8ft with funnel-shaped flowers of bright crimson, and a treasure of a cousin, *sperabile* of bell-shaped scarlet-crimson trumpets, which proved to be a first-class garden plant and won an Award of Merit. Another plant that won the Award was *Cyananthus lobatus* var. *farreri*, with flowers of deep sapphire blue. 'The finest I know,' was Farrer's claim for it. He found it sprawling on an alpine lawn at 13,000ft, though in Britain it is best grown as a scree plant. Its leaves are a decoration in themselves, lobed into featherings at the tips and clad with white hairs. The large single flower is somewhat like a periwinkle. Quite hardy too (though it cannot abide drought) is Farrer's *Cremanthodium delavayi*, a beautiful species 9–12in tall, with hanging heads of long rayed ragged flowers of citron-yellow.

Cox left for England in January 1920, Farrer deciding to remain for another season to continue his exploration of the Chinese frontier ranges from a point farther north than had been reached the year before. In the next nine months, of which two were spent in peace in a bungalow, he was to travel at least 1,000 miles, 600 of them on foot or pony-back, in that time collecting specimens of no fewer than 400 plants, writing his field notes, his articles for the *Gardeners Chronicle*, his diary and letters to his friends, a full-length novel and a volume of historical fantasies. Five of the nine months were spent in an unspeakable climate.

In 1919 he and Cox had made Hpimaw their centre, at the foot of one of the passes into China, and travelled from Myitkina north-east to Seliku, north up the Nmai River, due east to Htawgaw, and back to their base, with local excursions to the Chimili Valley farther to the north where they established a camp, and to the passes of Fung Schweling and Hpare in the south. They finally left Hpimaw on 18 November, travelling by train from the railhead at Myitkina to Rangoon, where they parted. Farrer now went back to Myitkina alone and found his servants waiting for him.

He headed north up the Mali River to Fort Hertz, then struck west to the Nmai by way of Konglu and up the Shingrup Kyet Pass. The bridge over the Nmai had been swept away and he forded the river with much difficulty. After following it downstream for some way he turned eastwards up its tributary, the Ah-Kyang, and reached Nyitadi. This was to be his base, and a leaky bamboo hut there his last home.

It was an exceptionally rainy season. Climbing up to camp on the heights, there was mist as well as rain, so that for three solid weeks he could not see more than a few yards ahead. Work became impossible, and when he descended again to Nyitadi – 'To see daylight and visible objects again was like having a load of lead lifted off,' he wrote.

He worked hard, and his men were willing. Nyitadi was situated within convenient reach of three passes and Farrer had set himself the task of visiting each of them three times in the course of the season. The bad weather and the strain told on him. On 1 October he fell ill with a cough and pains in the chest. His servant Bhaju made a fantastic non-stop journey of four days to Konglu to get a doctor, but on 17 October Farrer died. He was in the middle of the seed harvest, and what he had already collected and stored in his hut was left behind when they carried his body to Konglu. But from the few early seeds he sent home in 1920 are some gems. Among them were several rhododendrons: *tephropeplum* with its profusion of bell-shaped flowers varying from pink to carmine rose, its young leaves plum-purple beneath; *genestieranum*, distinctive for its racemes of small purple flowers; *protistum* of trusses of creamy white bells flushed with rose; the charming shrublet *charitopes* of apple-blossom pink bells speckled with crimson; the fragrant-clustered ivory beauty of *sino-nuttallii*, and *caloxanthum* which Farrer found on the open alpine slopes of Burma at 12,000ft. It is one of the prettiest of Reginald Farrer's introductions, with its clusters of flower-buds apricot, orange and vermilion opening to bells of pure canary yellow, and, with the flowers over, the almost cobalt-blue of its new young shoots.

There were two new cousins of the fritillary and lily, *Nomocharis basilissa* and *N. euxantha* var. *imberis*, the first scarlet and purple, the second yellow and crimson; and all over the Hpimaw hills on open slopes and in dells up to 8,000ft he had found yellow-and-white flowers that became gorgeous pokers of gaping vermilion receptacles, each containing three cones of contrasting crimson fruit. Thus did Farrer describe the handsome *Hedychium spicatum* var. *acuminatum*. There were three gentians. And there was *Cassiope selaginoides*, a hardy heath-like plant with tiny pinkish flowers nodding on inch-high stems, the sort of plant he would have cherished in his rock garden at Ingleborough, had he lived to see it grow there.

Reginald Farrer was a man who knew plants as few have ever known them. He lived with them intimately in the heights he called the eaves of the world, and not only did he give us some of our very finest garden plants but new eyes to see them in their real beauty, and an understanding to appreciate them as beings like ourselves. To him they were immortal. Out in Kansu he knew of the horrors of the 1914 war from the heart-rending letters of his friends, and it was his faith in the eternal life of plants in their cycle of birth and rebirth that caused him to write of them:

> All the wars of the world, all the Caesars, have not the staying power of a Lily in a cottage border. Man creates the storms in his teacup, and dies of them, but there remains a something standing outside, a something impregnable, as far beyond reach of man's destructiveness as is man's own self. The immortality of marvels and miseries is a vain, small thing compared to the immortality of a flower that blooms and is dead by dusk.

INDEX OF PLANTS

Italic figures denote illustrations

INDEX OF PEOPLE AND PLACES

Plant hunters' names and illustration pages in italic

206

INDEX OF PEOPLE AND PLACES